Tornado Watch #211

Also by John G. Fuller:

The Gentlemen Conspirators
The Money Changers
Incident at Exeter
The Interrupted Journey
The Great Soul Trial
The Day of Saint Anthony's Fire
200,000,000 Guinea Pigs
Arigo: Surgeon of the Rusty Knife
Fever: The Hunt for a New Killer Virus
We Almost Lost Detroit
The Ghost of Flight 401
The Poison That Fell from the Sky
The Airmen Who Would Not Die
Are the Kids All Right?
The Day We Bombed Utah

Tornado Watch #211

John G. Fuller

William Morrow and Company, Inc.

New York

Library of Congress Cataloging-in-Publication Data

Fuller, John Grant, 1913–
  Tornado watch #211.
  Includes index.
  1. Tornadoes—Ohio. 2. Tornadoes—Pennsylvania.
I. Title.
QC955.5.U6F95   1987   363.3 '492   87-7830
ISBN 0-688-06590-2

Printed in the United States of America

First Edition

1   2   3   4   5   6   7   8   9   10

BOOK DESIGN BY MELISSA FELDMAN

NA # 6941
(7046)

CONTENTS

1. /COLLISION COURSE

Days, weeks, before it happened, the frigid air mass formed over the frozen Arctic, an army mobilizing for a southward push. At the same time, over the warm waters of the Gulf of Mexico, great masses of moist, sultry air gathered to move northward. Continental-polar they called the first mass; maritime-tropical they called the second. Slowly, the two invisible armies began a collision course, thousands of miles away from each other. They were out of man's control.

But they could be tracked and observed. In fact, when forecaster Steve Weiss walked through the Art Deco halls of the Federal Building in Kansas City at 7:30 A.M. on Friday, May 31, 1985, he would be getting ready to do just that. It would be a race with the clock, as always. By the time he was in shirt-sleeves and sitting at his desk inside the horseshoe formed by the flickering screens of a half dozen computer terminals, he was already going over the charts and printouts with the midnight shift forecaster, Larry Wilson.

Wilson's briefing there at the National Severe Storms Forecast Center highlighted a moderate risk for severe thunderstorms from the Great Lakes and upper Ohio Valley eastward. The word "moderate" was misleading. The official scale runs from slight to moderate to high. But as one forecaster put it facetiously, " 'Moderate' means a death knell—dive for the cellar."

Exaggeration or not, there was more than just something in the air as Steve Weiss scanned the radar and satellite screens that day. He pulled a half dozen charts and printouts in front of him and analyzed them quickly. Handsome, alert, with a British military moustache, Weiss moved with sureness and speed as he drew the curves that defined the frontal boundaries and shaped the equivalent of a topographical map of the weather across the country. The picture that emerged was not a pretty one. But even forecaster Weiss could not yet know that one of the most devastating families of tornadoes in the country's history was in the making.

Seven hundred miles to the east of Kansas City, at the base of the chimney of western Pennsylvania and not far from Erie, is the placid little town of Albion. At the time that Steve Weiss was well into his computations at the National Severe Storms Forecast Center, Linda Quay was marshaling her three children, Billy, ten; Michael, five; and Bonnie Sue, nearly two, for breakfast. It was the normal beginning of an average day, with Bonnie Sue squealing in her high chair, and Billy and Michael downing their cereal in front of the TV set. Their house was modest, trim, and sturdy on South Park Avenue, one of a dozen frame houses set neatly in a row.

The biggest event of the day was a T-ball game scheduled for early evening—a little Little League sort of competition for kindergarten tots like Michael. There is no pitcher. The ball is simply placed on a post for the batter to hit.

It was raining, however, and prospects looked dim for the game to be played, much to Michael's disappointment. Perhaps, Linda thought, the rain would stop later to clear both the skies and Michael's mood.

Through the open arch between the dining room and the living room, Linda paid special attention to the weather report. The jovial Willard Scott was on the *Today* show screen. Scott was talking about the weather in Texas. The forecast did not look good there: tornadoes were distinctly possible down in the Lone Star State.

With nothing but the rain to be concerned about in Pennsylvania, Linda chuckled and said to her children: "Hey, kids, aren't you glad we don't live in Texas and don't have to worry about a tornado?"

Throughout the day, the weather was skittish. One neighbor told Linda the day seemed ominously strange. But the sun was peeking in and out during the morning, and Linda thought little more about the weather. She turned her attention to housework and to taking care of five-year-old Michael and baby-sitting little Andrea Sobol, a neighbor's child from two houses away.

A few blocks away, on the corner of East Pearl and Thornton, Sandra Stahlsmith was going through much the same routine. She had her hands full with five energetic youngsters to handle, with daughters of nine, eight, and one, and two boys, Zachary, three; and Luke, six. Luke was a little late for elementary school, and she whisked him off before she turned to her chores. She, too, was baby-sitting for a neighbor, a frisky one-year-old, a common practice in the town, where mutual help is taken for granted.

Elsewhere, things were quiet enough in the rolling, wooded hills of the surrounding countryside, broken by the lush, green pastures of the Amish farms scattered around the town. Along the straight, undulating ribbon of U.S. 6N that leads to Albion, a few fragile black carriages of the Amish braved the traffic moving ten times their speed. They were guarded only by a fluorescent red triangle mounted on the rear. Some were on the way to a quilting bee, others to a barn-raising or cake sale.

The Amish are a sturdy lot, the Pennsylvania Germans known as Pennsylvania Dutch, fearing God, tilling the land with God-given talent, garbed in black with wide-brimmed hats, and with wide-open smiles evident once their shyness and their thick chin beards are brushed aside. Generous in offering help to each other—and to neighboring outsiders, whom they call the "English"—they still shun electricity, radios, TV, tractors, and cars. And they also shun their fellow progressive Amish, called Beachy

Amish, who have let down the barriers on those modern intrusions of the material world.

In the village center on Market Street, editor Bob McClymond sat in front of his battered Royal typewriter at the *Albion News,* ready to chronicle the events of the week, from a chicken-and-biscuit luncheon at the Methodist church to a flea market sale at the Circle B Saddle Club. A sensitive, intelligent man, McClymond enjoyed his role as a country editor. He also enjoyed the town, in spite of the stress of lost industry, of the railroad that had once been its lifeblood, of the Erie Canal that had launched its early growth. His paper was modern, progressive, professional, and cleanly set. His editorials were firm but affectionate, headed by Voltaire's famous utterance: "I disapprove of what you say, but I will defend to the death your right to say it."

Albion was settled in 1815 long after bitter struggles with the Iroquois tribes, with the Indians scalping whites and the whites scalping Indians. But on May 31, 1985, savagery of a different nature would again visit the region. On the morning of that day, however, Albion, with its two thousand citizens, was a Norman Rockwell oil painting of a typical American town.

At intervals during the last week in May, the weather across the country had been fitful, if not freakish. Pushed by the cold frontal polar air mass, a snowstorm dumped several feet of snow on Mount Evans in Colorado on Thursday, May 30. The same snow hit Montana and Wyoming, while it whipped up seventy-mile-an-hour winds in Nebraska. Blinding clouds of dust closed a major highway there. Record hundred-degree heat seared Texas, Oklahoma, and Kansas, while thunderstorms reached from Missouri to Wisconsin, and eastward to the Ohio Valley

Unconfirmed tornadoes were said to have touched down in parts of Ohio, but no damage was reported. Nineteen other touchdowns of twisters churned portions of Minnesota, Iowa, and Missouri. Three people were injured. Thirty houses were damaged. Just outside Kansas City, a Ford Motor assembly plant was battered by hail the size of baseballs. It smashed windows and punched dents into over a thousand new cars in the parking area.

The polar army air mass on its way to collision with the tropical army from the Gulf was becoming an enemy of the people, ravaging the countryside in its march.

But it still was withholding its heavy artillery. Flash flood warnings went out in eastern Ohio and western Pennsylvania from local weather stations. But the outlook in the region was typified by the weather report in Friday's *Youngstown Vindicator:* "A flash flood watch is in effect for this afternoon as the threat of showers and thunderstorms, possibly severe at times, continues at least through early evening. For tonight, the showers could be lingering, but much better weather will develop by Saturday, with a return of mostly sunny skies and lower humidity."

For campers, fishermen, swimmers, and picnickers heading for the ample state forests and lakes of the region, the weekend outlook was welcome. A few preliminary showers would simply clear the air, even if they rumbled a bit on Friday evening. Saturday's "sunny skies and lower humidity" would more than make up for the inconvenience. Meanwhile, the dense cold front moved eastward, bulldozing the warmer air up into the sky, forming giant castles of cumulonimbus clouds ahead of it, each packed with lethal energy boiling within it.

Back in Kansas City, with the air masses stratified like layer cakes from the tropopause at some sixty thousand feet on down, forecaster Steve Weiss was simultaneously juggling a confusing array of parameters, vertical and horizontal. He was dealing with a four-dimensional problem, with the time factor every bit as important as the width, length, and breadth of the air masses.

Was the jet stream strong, capping the approaching cold and warm air masses? What about instability and moisture? Was there dry, hot air above a moisture layer? Were there strong low-pressure areas developing? Would the dense cold front army nose beneath the approaching warm front, continuing to push it up in the air to produce those towering cumulonimbus clouds with anvil heads that could spike at times beyond the tropopause up to seventy thousand feet and up to ten miles in diameter? This is the inevitable habit of fast-moving cold fronts, the ultimate and often awesome outcome of the collision course. A single severe thunderstorm supercell can hold more energy than a hydrogen bomb.

Steve Weiss looked over the surface chart drawn up by the midnight shift an hour before his arrival. It showed a deep low over western upper Michigan, with the cold front arcing across lower Michigan and parts of Illinois and Arkansas. There was the very warm air mass coming up from the Gulf ahead of the cold front. Other data showed that winds aloft were sweeping toward the Great Lakes and Ohio Valley as high as 126 knots at the upper jet stream level.

The threat of severe thunderstorms was clearly there. Eastern Ohio and western Pennsylvania appeared to be the major targets of the highly unstable weather, although the worst threat appeared to be north of the border, in Ontario.

The meteorologists at the National Severe Storms Forecast Center in Kansas City have been called "keepers of the gates of hell." This is not a misnomer. Tornadoes are the worst killers that weather can produce. They are the harpies of the severe thunderstorm supercells. They scream down from the bellies of towering cumulonimbus clouds in the form of obscene snakes or elephant trunks, alternately spitting out unmeasured winds and sucking up anything from the eyes of geese to a railroad car.

At the center, tornadoes were the worst enemy. Fred Ostby, congenial chief of the Kansas City operation, had been battling against their unpredictability for years. At the age of fifty-five, he was able to give vent to his daily fight with the weather as a full-fledged ice hockey player with the Kansas City Amateur Hockey League. He enjoyed playing with his two grown sons. He was also a pilot and a Rocky Mountain trekker. With what was left of his spare time, he shaped highly technical articles for the American Meteorological Society.

Along with his deputy director, Ed Ferguson, he worried about the tornado fatalities that inevitably followed in the wake of a serious outbreak. Ferguson, out of Florida State and Oklahoma universities, joined him in that outlook. Both had been steeped in weather lore since their early years. Ostby had known his destiny since elementary school. The stars and moon were sources of wonderment then, and later he came down to the clouds, setting up weather measuring equipment in his yard, leading to his master's degree in meteorology at New York University in 1960. The great hurricane of 1938 also left a deep impression on him.

Ferguson, growing up on a Missouri farm, knew firsthand the devastation of tornadoes. When a tornado wiped out a neighboring town, killing fourteen, his father became almost paranoid. At the slightest sign of a heavy storm, he would be off to the sloping door of the storm cellar with blankets and food and a long-handled ax to chop his way out if necessary. Ferguson also had a friend who saw a tornado coming toward his house. He was sowing oats at the time, and he dashed for cover. He never made it. He was found dead without a mark on his body. The tiny oat seeds had been driven through his skull and into his brain.

Like many in the National Weather Service, both were ignited by early experiences, early impressions. Both would rather face a hurricane than a tornado. A hurricane moves slowly. It is easily tracked. There is plenty of time for a warning. Tornadoes, like hidden snipers, fire out of hiding. Only the general location of their hideouts can be known, and many of those fail to produce the expected disaster. Ostby did not like to cry wolf.

Ostby was concerned over two problems. There was the technical problem of trying to put out a fast and accurate forecast. There was the problem of convincing the public it ought to be ready—and to know what to do. He agreed with the sociologists. Many people will do almost anything they can to deny that they're under risk. If the warning is for Kansas, it can't happen in Missouri. If the neighbor down the street doesn't go to his basement, why should I?

The syndrome was especially true in places where tornadoes rarely hit. In the Tornado Alley of the Great Plains, the audience was attentive to tornado and severe thunderstorm watches and warnings. They had faced tragedy too many times. In the East, the picture was different. Tornadoes were rare. But when they hit, they hit hard. The population is more dense. Indifference is widespread. The key thought: It can't happen here.

Statistically, the attitude was not unfounded. Thunderstorms are common, over a hundred thousand a year. Only a thousand or less carry tornadoes. Most of these are weak. There is an average of only twenty-five killer tornadoes a year. But they account for about 80 percent of the people killed.

As he made his way toward the bullpen where Steve Weiss was working that morning of May 31, Ostby had a lot on his mind. Clearly the cold front was moving eastward, and the warm front northward, moisture-laden and unstable. There was bound to be convergence on the low levels of the atmosphere, and that meant updrafts. They, in turn, meant trouble. The main question was where and when.

In front of the flickering computer terminals, Weiss was running his race against time. The official Severe Weather Outlook Report was due to go out over the wires at ten that morning. Hundreds of weather stations in the United States, Canada, and Mexico would be waiting for the report. The problem was always that Weiss and his colleagues had to assess small-scale phenomena from large-scale data. Wistfully, Weiss often wished there were a weather cookbook, where he could go down a list of things, mix them, and come up with magic data. Even with computers, radar, and satellite pictures, it was a question of beating the clock in the face of the welter of data that had to be absorbed quickly

But Weiss liked the challenge, liked the pressure, liked the job, wherein he could help a community in a life-or-death situation, even if it were hundreds of miles or even a thousand miles away from him. Each day was different. Each day presented a science detective story that had to be solved. Like his colleagues, he was fascinated with the giant thunderstorms he faced in his routine. They were his mortal enemies. And he respected them. The frustration came in that he could act only as an advance scout. But that at least could play a critical role in a life-threatening situation.

Although he had no real early traumatic experience, as Ferguson did, Weiss was fascinated with weather from his early school days in Chicago, where he kept weather records; he later moved on to meteorology at Oklahoma and to UCLA for his master's degree. On the job at the National Severe Storms Forecast Center, he found deep personal satisfaction. He would ask himself constantly after issuing a severe storm or tornado watch: What could we have done better? What did we fail to do today?

The irony is that, despite all the scientific advancements during the twentieth century, tornadoes still present the ultimate challenge to the meteorologist. Their predictability remains almost as mysterious and elusive as the dream of the Unified Theory of Relativity was to Einstein, or as the complete conquest of cancer is to medical science.

Radar, satellite, computers, twice-a-day radiosonde readings from weather balloons, and other sophisticated instruments have brought great strides in predicting the probability of and the general areas where tornadoes may strike. Plans of the National Weather Service for the future promise to fine-tune tornado watches and warnings even more, in less than a decade from now. But exactly what geographic point an individual tornado might strike will still have to remain almost as unpredictable as a lightning bolt.

By the time Weiss was ready to dispatch his countrywide official Severe Weather Outlook Report at ten that morning, tornadoes were very much on his mind. SVR TSTMS—the National Weather Service-elided nomenclature for severe thunderstorms—appeared reasonably certain by late afternoon and early evening over the Ohio Valley and western Pennsylvania, with a very moist and unstable air mass ahead of the cold front. Rising temperatures in the afternoon would warm the ground and increase the threat. With the strong jet flow aloft, the storms ahead of and along the front could move eastward at almost turnpike speed.

When Fred Ostby joined Weiss by the computer terminals, they flipped through the layers of charts in front of them. Their attention centered on three main areas of concern: the strength of the jet stream, the resulting instability with dry air coming in above the surface moisture, and the strength of the storm system. They had plenty of tools to work with—but there was still the overriding necessity of human judgment. There was the basic synoptic surface chart. It was peppered with the dots representing the National Weather Service offices across the continent. Each dot had miniature feathery flags indicating wind speed and direction, and coded numbers to give temperature, visibility, dew point, barometric pressure, and other indicators at each locality. The charts Weiss worked with were computerized projections furnished by the National Meteorological Center in Washington. But he preferred to connect the isobars and fill in the small wind flags manually to get a firsthand feel of the situation.

There were also the vertical development charts, the stability charts, the thickness charts for the lower half of the atmosphere, and the numerical model facsimile charts to cope with. It was a confusing array that the center continually handled with authority mixed with a certain amount of humility. Under the daily pressures and responsibilities, Ostby and Weiss both confessed that Mother Nature never let them get big heads. They were always hoping the data would be more clear-cut. But the data seldom were.

Not even the satellite picture could unravel the whole mystery. The GOES weather spacecraft looks down from Olympian heights, 23,300 miles above the earth in geostationary orbit. Its spinning radiometer photographs nearly a quarter of the surface of the earth every eighteen minutes. To all but the expert eye, the fluffy clouds appeared quite innocent. But to Weiss and Ostby, the picture reflected a dense cold front. It sliced down through a wide territory from Ontario hundreds of miles to the Great Lakes southward almost to Tennessee. Still there was that puzzling lack of activity over eastern Ohio and western Pennsylvania—where everything should be happening but nothing was.

The decision to issue a tornado watch was often an agonizing one. As Weiss put it, "It would be nice to be able to say, 'between three-thirty and four P.M., this town is going to get hit.' That could save lives. But this is well beyond our capabilities, and it may be for quite a while."

Working with Ostby, Weiss continued to shuffle his charts, assessing each one in a fraction of a minute. From the data it was clear they would have to keep monitoring the trouble spots carefully. It was important to narrow down the area where the severe weather would strike. They could never be 100 percent sure, especially when the few miles' difference in prognosis could spell the difference between alerting the wrong area and not alerting the area that should be. It was never certain. Typically, there would be doubts. One thing was certain that morning: There was going to be trouble.

Finally Weiss pointed to the Ohio Valley and western Pennsylvania.

"Looks definitely favorable," Weiss told him.

"It sure does," Ostby said. "It looks real good."

But they were talking in severe weather forecast inverted language. "Favorable" and "good" mean only that the conditions are favorable and good for intensely bad weather—not at all good for the land or people that lay below the weather. Ostby agreed that a moderately severe thunderstorm watch should go out, although he wished there were more public understanding that "moderately severe" called for extreme caution in the areas involved. There would be no tornado watch at this time, however. The potential was there, but the clues still were not solid enough.

The data on charts and screens were so massive that Weiss was losing his race with time. He was finally ready at 10:14 A.M. Central Daylight Time, being meticulously careful not to over- or underalarm the areas some six hundred to seven hundred miles to the east. He slid his chair over the carpeted floor to the dispatch terminal keyboard and typed with brisk two-finger speed:

MDT RISK OF SVR TSTMS THIS AFTN AND ERY TNGT OVR OH . . . WRN AND CNTRL NY . . . WRN AND CNTRL PA . . . VERY MOIST AND UNSTBL AMS PRESENT AHD OF CDNT . . . SVR TSTMS EXPCD TO RDVLP ALG/AHD OF CDENT . . .

In less cryptic words, the risk of Ohio and western Pennsylvania and New York being hit with severe thunderstorms was almost inevitable, with the moist and unstable air mass in front of the cold front and ready to collide with it.

The dispatch went out instantaneously to all the forecast offices across the country on the electronic system known as AFOS, the Automation of Field Offices and Services. No mention of a tornado watch could be made until further evidence showed up. A false alarm would make a real alarm far less effective. And every field office knew that "moderate" risk carried a lot more weight than the dictionary implied.

2. / THE ENEMY FORMS

The focal point of the threatened area happened to fall in the region that was known as the Connecticut Western Reserve in Ohio, plus a thick slice of western Pennsylvania just over the border to the east. Both regions were rich in history, as turbulent as the thunder cells that were approaching them on May 31, 1985.

As far back as 1630, the Crown generously granted the citizens of Connecticut a westward extension of its borders. Unsurveyed and unmapped by the king's men, Connecticut found itself in theoretical possession of a ribbon of land between the 41st and 42nd parallels that ran from the Atlantic "all the way to the South Seas." It was a thin ribbon, however. In depth this would range roughly from the shores of Lake Erie south to the present-day Youngstown, some eighty miles deep of what was called "good and promised land," with soil so rich it "needed only to be tickled with a hoe to laugh with the harvest," as one eloquent early settler put it. He didn't need to mention the rich fur and timber harvest that awaited anyone who could swing an ax or fire a musket.

Pennsylvania had no intention of providing the Connecticut

frontiersmen with a royal road to the West. The New Englanders eventually had to settle for a modest parcel of geography that began at the Pennsylvania-Ohio border and stretched only to a point 120 miles westward. This "New Connecticut" became a mixed blessing for the settlers and traders. Although there were rumors of corn growing fourteen feet high and vegetables growing like weeds, there was a generous supply of Frenchmen and Indians to block the path. The Indians were rather hospitable at first—until encroachments and broken pledges by the land-hungry Yankees unleashed their wrath.

The early Erie Indians built burial mounds, later blended in with the Iroquois nations. Deprived of their lands, their vengeance was fierce. As hordes of frontiersmen swarmed across the border to wipe out their hunting grounds and burn their crops and villages, the great chief Pontiac united the many tribes to try in turn to wipe out all the whites east of the Alleghenies. Traders were scalped, their hearts torn out and eaten. In return, Indian scalps brought the colonists a bounty of 130 pieces of eight.

Meanwhile, the French and English battled between themselves over the rich fur trade. In 1794, Mad Anthony Wayne broke up the Indian confederation in the Battle of Fallen Timbers. After the War of 1812, "Ohio Fever" took over. Back in the East, villages were literally depopulated as wagons rolled westward.

Just over the border in Pennsylvania, the settlers fared no better in their sanguinary battles with the French and Indians—and even with the Connecticut intruders. Although eventually the tribes for the most part were herded unceremoniously out to questionable hunting grounds in the far West, the Pennsylvanians willingly risked their own scalps to set up their own happier hunting grounds. If they didn't realize their own importance, Voltaire did, back in the comfort of civilized France. Voltaire noted: "Such are the complications of international politics that a shot fired in the remote wilderness of western Pennsylvania could give the signal that could set Europe ablaze."

This didn't quite happen, but by 1800 the stage was set for towns and cities to blossom in the wilderness in lands that experienced extravagant prosperity alternately raked with ravages

of both Nature and man. First forests were slaughtered by frontiersmen who could split a hundred rails a day, until 90 percent
of the timberland was gone. Then the great flash floods came.
They drowned prosperous Dayton three times in the period from
1814 to 1913. Then came the flood of immigrants in the 1840s—
Irish, Germans, Polish, Slavs, Italians, and others. They brought
new blood, new vigor to the melting pot, often in the face of
ungentlemanly prejudice.

Then came the railroads, with the 1877 strike appropriately
called hell on wheels. The ensuing riots didn't bother magnate
Jay Gould. "Hell," he said, "I can hire one half of the working
class to kill the other half." Less than a decade later, the coal
miners struck and started an underground fire in the mines in
1884 that raged uncontrolled for decades. Steel had its share of
turbulence. The Youngstown strike in 1914 brought riot, death,
and destruction. It was repeated in 1937, with fifty thousand
miners out, seven killed, and over three hundred wounded by the
state militia.

And before the Great Depression sent its wave of economic
disaster over the land, a killer tornado struck northern Ohio on
the shores of Lake Erie. It killed seventy-five and injured over
a thousand. It was only a harbinger of others to follow, including
the 1974 twister that almost blotted out Xenia, Ohio, population
twenty-seven thousand.

Just over the border to the east, Pennsylvania provided almost
a carbon copy of Ohio's fortunes and misfortunes. The bloodshed
of the battles with the cunning and fierce Seneca tribe in the
1650s carried through to General Braddock's defeat and the re-
venge by the Indians. Great whirlwinds, as tornadoes were then
called, blasted the Pennsylvania landscape just below Erie over a
wide area. Undaunted, the Pennsylvanians and ex-Colonial soldiers staked out their homesteads. The pioneers flooded through
in Lancaster-made Conestoga wagons on their way to the West.
The stagecoaches followed, then the railroads, along with the
rich discovery of oil and coal, then the puddling of iron and the
rolling of iron bars to make Pittsburgh the world center of Big
and Little Steel.

The Homestead strike in the early 1890s brought pitched battles between hired killers and striking workers, fanning out to over fifty strikes throughout the state. The steel companies breathed in and out with good times and bad times, which left the mills dead and black and the workers gaunt and breadless.

Nature was no less brutal to Pennsylvania than it was to Ohio. On May 31, 1889—the same day of the year that the meteorologists in Kansas City were worrying about the apparent tornado target area in these regions—the citizens of Johnstown, Pennsylvania, were worried about the great South Fork dam. It held back nearly eighty million tons of water, and it furnished the happy fishing grounds for a group of millionaires that included Andrew Carnegie and Andrew Mellon. The club was urged to lift an iron screen to relieve the mounting pressure, but it held back doing so because the treasured black bass would escape. The dam burst. The houses of Johnstown crumbled like matchsticks. Over two thousand drowned. In the same year, the worst tornado to date hit western Pennsylvania, and other flash floods took lives and property throughout the state.

Through it all, from the earliest days of expansion, Erie sat on the edge of Lake Erie at the top of the "chimney" of Pennsylvania. As the northernmost city of the state, it furnished its only port on the Great Lakes. Here was the funnel for import and export, buttressed by the Erie-Pittsburgh Canal, which pumped industrial blood southward down through both Ohio and Pennsylvania. On May 31, 1985, the city was destined to play an important part in another drama, which would match much of the turbulence of the state's early history.

The Erie airport lies less than thirty miles northeast of the town of Albion, where Linda Quay and Sandra Stahlsmith were hustling their children off to school, where Bob McClymond was pounding out his news stories on his ancient typewriter, where the Amish were moving along the roads in their fragile black carriages. Erie houses the National Weather Service for the Erie region, covering nine of the northwestern counties of Pennsylvania. It sits in a trim modern building near the hangars and runways. Its parking sign for one section of the lot reflects a yeasty sense of humor for the visitor: DON'T EVEN THINK OF PARKING HERE.

Dave Bell, a latter-day transplant from Connecticut, is the tall, husky chief of the office, working with his staff of meteorologists on alternating shifts. He arrived at 7:20 A.M. on Friday, May 31, 1985, to go over the outlook with forecaster Bob Sandstrom. Both combine a droll sense of whimsy with a seriousness of purpose characteristic of most in the National Weather Service. The frustration of facing the puckish vicissitudes of the weather on a daily basis requires both qualities.

As far back as Tuesday, Erie had been keeping a weather eye on the cold front as it moved across the country, sweeping out of the Great Plains from west to east. The savage storms in Colorado, Montana, and Nebraska and the blistering hail in Kansas City on Thursday did not escape notice. Now, on Friday, it clearly looked as if a moment of truth was brewing.

When Sandstrom reviewed the early-morning Kansas City data from the National Severe Storms Forecast Center, he and Bell agreed that everything looked ripe and "nice"—again inverted meteorological language—for hefty severe thunderstorms in their region. Steve Weiss's Severe Weather Outlook Report from Kansas City clearly meant serious business. It outlined a neat box on the map that made the Erie area a sharp target for the "gates of hell" to open up on.

In fact, it looked like a perfect scenario for the worst in the Erie region: The swift cold front was coming in from the West, with muscular winds behind it. Its leading edge of dry air was ready to confront the saturated humid air from the Gulf. But the kicker was that nothing was really happening. The local Erie radar screen was clear as a bell. By the time the early-afternoon outlook dispatch came in from Kansas City, neither Bell nor Sandstrom was surprised to see that the severe thunderstorm watch had been downgraded to a "slight" risk—the lowest order on the totem pole.

But the early-afternoon dispatch from Kansas City did not show total optimism. It read:

AIR MASS STILL QUITE UNSTABLE SO ISOLATED SE-
VERE THUNDERSTORMS STILL POSSIBLE THROUGHOUT
THE REGION.

Erie would not be letting down its guard, especially since some
backbreaking thunderstorms were threatening to come eastward
into Ontario, just to the north.

Down in Albion John Halfast, another meteorologist for the
Erie National Weather Service, was relaxing at his home. He
would be coming on duty at four in the afternoon, until midnight.
He noted the hot and sultry day. The air was still and oppressive.
The sun was bright and scorching. His wife, who had once lived
in tornado country, leaned on her feminine intuition and said,
"John, this is just the way it felt before tornadoes hit. You can
feel it in the air." Halfast would be interested in checking her
prognosis when he went on duty later in the day.

In spite of the turbulent history that raged on both sides of it,
the Ohio-Pennsylvania border cuts a straight, razor-sharp line
almost due south from Lake Erie down to the West Virginia
border. In the process it cuts through the Pymatuning State Park,
shared by both states. Here, where the strange burial mounds
blend with the old trails of the Iroquois Indians, the woods are
lovely, dark, and deep and the waters of the imposing Pymatuning
Lake are sparkling. It is a score of miles southwest of Erie.

While the meteorologists of Kansas City and the Erie weather
station were pondering the puzzling weather conditions of Friday, May 31, the boaters, swimmers, picknickers, and campers
were just beginning to filter into the park shores and woodlands
for the weekend. The early Memorial Day had jammed the
Linesville campgrounds at the northern end of the park with over
a hundred families the previous weekend. But on this day the
park rangers and the hostess at the campgrounds expected less
than a third of that.

A dozen miles to the south, at the park office, Gene Hart,
assistant park superintendent, agreed with the estimate. The
sun was going in and out, but the weather seemed skittish, with

an unpromising outlook. In fact, Hart had picked up a commercial forecast from Youngstown that mentioned the severe-weather possibility. As he entered headquarters that morning, he sensed something eerie about the climate, but he didn't quite know why.

In Jamestown, a handful of miles south of the park, Harold McCrea, a salty metalworker recently retired from U.S. Steel, found the weather to his liking. He set his schedule for the day—repairing chain saws and polishing up his shiny camper in his yard. As he put an aluminum ladder up the side of the camper, the sun peeked out and he said to his wife, Freda, "Looks like a nice day after all."

Freda wasn't entirely sure. "I don't know," she said. "What's it feel like before a tornado?"

"There's a nice breeze going," her husband answered. "Tornado you get a real still calm just before. Real calm."

Freda, half embarrassed because she had no idea why she brought the subject up, went back into the house.

About seventy miles due west of the Pennsylvania border that shares Lake Pymatuning with Ohio, Marvin Miller, chief of the National Weather Service at Cleveland-Hopkins International Airport, kept a continuing watch on the radar screen and the dispatches from Kansas City. A tall, bespectacled man with a well-scrubbed visage, he agreed with a comment from one of his forecasters, Jack May, that May 31 might be wet enough to take a goldfish for a walk.

Miller wasn't surprised when he got a call at seven-forty that morning from Jerry Murphy. Murphy was a pleasantly gruff ex-Sea Bee, and a ham radio operator for a quarter century. He was one of the three thousand volunteer spotters for the National Weather Service across the country. Together they made up a network called Skywarn. Their services were invaluable in fanning out severe-weather watches and warnings to the public, in radio communications when wires were down, and in mounting observation posts to bring what is called the "ground truth" to the weather stations—what is actually happening on the ground that doesn't show up in the red and green globs on radar or the broad scope of the satellite image.

Murphy's specialty was ham radio. Many weather station offices provide a special desk for the Skywarn volunteers who come in during severe weather to man the post. Murphy had an uncanny weather sense in addition to his radio expertise. He also was skilled in coordinating several hundred amateur radio operators in the counties under the Erie station umbrella.

"Just wanted to know when you wanted me to come in this morning," Murphy told Miller over the phone.

"Well," said Miller, "we just might be able to use you today."

"Looks favorable, then?" Murphy asked. Murphy, like the rest of them, used the meteorologist's reverse terminology for "bad."

"This might be the one we've been looking for," Miller told him. Murphy didn't need to be told that this time of year was the highest risk for tornadoes—or at least severe weather. "Could be as early as ten A.M. Might not be until late in the day."

"Be in about eight-thirty," Murphy said, and he hung up.

Chief Marvin Miller, like every other weather station chief in the country, leaned heavily on the work that men like Murphy performed. Miller himself spent considerable time giving talks and training sessions not only to the spotter and ham radio network but also to police, highway patrols, fire departments, and schools to prepare the public for weather emergencies. Although severe storms and tornadoes were less numerous in his Ohio region than in the Great Plains states, those that had hit in the past had brought a greater than average death toll and damage because of the higher population concentration.

Only a few weeks before May 31, Miller was saying on his public talk circuit that the local region had experienced large multiple tornado outbreaks every eight or ten years. "I don't like to say this," Miller had concluded his public talks, "but I'm afraid we're due for another outbreak of killer tornadoes this spring. We want you to be ready for it."

Miller focused many of his talks on schools. The kids were more responsive than adults, he found. During some tornadoes in the past, the children actually instructed their parents exactly what to do: Go quickly to the cellar, to the southwest corner and protect the head; go to an inside wall with no windows if there was no cellar. He wished there were statistics that showed how many lives had been saved because of the alertness of the children.

From all the data on the morning of May 31, Miller reached the unmistakable conclusion that something was going to happen, but neither he nor his staff nor his instruments could yet tell just where or when. There was no doubt it was an unusual day. At 10:00 A.M., Miller put in a call to the Kansas City center and asked Bill Sammler, assistant forecaster, how things looked. Sammler pointed out that the low-pressure area aloft was expected to move rapidly across the Great Lakes region and the Ohio Valley. A few hours later, however, Kansas City was able to report that the "moderate" risk could be dropped to "slight."

Forecaster Jack May, on duty at the radar and alphanumeric terminals, was puzzled. He was set up and ready for anything to happen, but the downgrading of the risk made it look as if they could relax a bit. Joining him at the screens, Jerry Murphy was a little disappointed that he had canceled his electrical contract customers for the day. The "ground truth" when he arrived at the station seemed to have turned benign: a hot sun and almost spotless blue skies. They belied the consensus that the storm-tracking instruments all through the region were showing: The dew points, where the moisture in the air suddenly changes from vapor to liquid, were ominous. The sun was baking the ground. This should be lifting the heavy moisture in the air. It didn't seem to be doing so.

At the Skywarn volunteer spotter desk, Murphy chatted over the radio with a dozen hams throughout the Cleveland area. Some of them had their own readings on barometric pressure, temperature, and other data. But none had a clue as to why the weather seemed so stable.

If a tornado watch did come in from Kansas City, or if the "ground truth" of an actual tornado did materialize from a trained spotter, the prescription for action was already set. A dispatch would go out immediately over the AFOS system, computer to computer. This system, known as the Automation of Field Offices and Services, permitted both text and graphics to be transmitted rapidly among the weather offices. The forecasters could quickly prepare, edit, and transmit forecasts, as well as punch up dozens of weather maps and other forecasts.

The National Oceanic and Atmospheric Administration (known as NOAA) weather wire teletypes would chatter, fanning out to 150 news outlets, where an alert bell would ring until shut off manually. The NOAA weather radio would immediately broadcast the warning to all radios equipped to receive it, again with a tone alert signal. The Emergency Broadcasting System, connected by a hotline, would break into any programs with the warning. Specially designated commercial stations are assigned this, in this case WWWE in Cleveland and WKBS in Youngstown. One phone call would be made to the county sheriff's office in each county, which would in turn notify its radio cars, plus fire and local police departments. There was a direct computer tie-up with the Ohio Highway Patrol. Then, of course, the Skywarn system would be alerted by radio through weather office volunteers such as Jerry Murphy.

It was a highly complex system, an interactive system between man and instrument. It wasn't perfect by any means. Often it was frustrating and agonizing. All this had to be handled under great pressure, and often with a lean and hungry staff at the weather office.

With the air in the region loaded with moisture, Marvin Miller kept a close check on the radar and satellite imagery throughout the morning. He was dumbfounded that nothing was showing on the screen under the conditions. The sun continued to dominate everything. There were practically no clouds. Miller began to feel a little sheepish about the zone forecasts Cleveland had issued earlier in the day: a flash flood watch at 3:32 A.M.; a severe storm possibility issued at 5:56 A.M. False alerts weakened the real alerts when they came along. They reinforced the public's can't-happen-to-me syndrome.

But the downgrading of the severe weather on the outlook from the National Severe Storms Forecast Center received at 3:30 P.M. in Cleveland did not look as if it was going to hold. The cold front was moving northeastward on an arc from Sandusky in the north to Cincinnati in the south. The air coming up from the Gulf was so unstable that the slightest trigger could set off towering supercell cumulonimbus clouds, each a potential nursemaid for a brood of tornadoes that might be spit out separately.

Still, the radar screens in the targeted areas continued to remain clear; they showed absolutely no activity, not even minor showers. In spite of the ominous signs that had been alternately building and fading through the day, Miller finally concluded at 3:30 P.M. that he could relax for the upcoming weekend. As a skilled amateur cabinetmaker, he looked forward to finishing up the last touches of a grandfather clock he was building, especially enjoying the rich scent of the black walnut wood he was working with. Jerry Murphy decided to return to his shop to prepare his electrical contracting work for the next day. Jack May got ready to enjoy a relaxing weekend with his family.

As 4:00 P.M. approached, tornadoes looked less and less probable that day. Miller, along with Murphy and Jack May, studied the radar screen for a final look. It seemed incredible, but only a tiny pinpoint of a shower was showing up within a wide hundred-mile area. It was insignificant. It looked as if everyone could breathe easier.

Back over the Pennsylvania border, just to the southeast of Pymatuning State Park and just west of Jamestown, Pennsylvania, is the tiny, proud town of Atlantic. It is hard to find on the map. There is no route number on the thin strips of back roads that lead to it over the lush green hills, checkerboarded with thick clusters of evergreen and hardwood trees. On top of one hill, a towering landmark stands over the town: the AT&T 312-foot-high microwave relay tower, a massive steel giant that can be seen for miles. The trim, manicured farms are widely scattered, each with a tall, domed silo, the bulk of them owned by industrious Amish farmers. As in the Albion area, the Amish shun electricity, motorcars, and tractors. Conspicuously absent are TV antennae or electrical and phone lines leading to the farmhouses. Concessions to the material world include pressurized Coleman gasoline lanterns and gasoline-powered washing machines. In the Amish school yards, girls with long gray dresses play volleyball, while the boys in wide hats and overalls romp on the softball field.

The largest building in town is the Atlantic Congregational Church, under the energetic guidance of Reverend Charles Polley, well respected by both Amish and non-Amish. The Amish themselves require no church; they meet in alternating homes for worship.

Reverend Polley was having a busy day on May 31, with multiple errands to do in nearby Meadville and Greenville, a few miles away from Atlantic. Ammon Miller, a sturdy Amishman with a typical Lincolnesque beard, a wide straw hat, and a twinkle in his eyes, was working near Atlantic helping to build prefab houses. He alternated that occupation with his farming at home with his wife, Elizabeth, and two boys, seventeen and fifteen.

During the morning, he worked indoors. When he went to the fields in the afternoon, he noticed an oppressive, sultry feeling in the air that was extremely odd. Sweat came easily with the slightest effort.

Elsewhere in the Amish sector of the community, the farmers went quietly about their work behind horse-drawn plows. Among them were Andrew Byler and Bishop Edward Yoder, who blended his pastoral work with expert carpentry and farming. On this day, Bishop Yoder was helping to build a home for a neighbor in a nearby town. Elderly Andrew Byler was doing his light chores at home. Neither noticed anything unusual about the weather except that it was hot and steamy. Atlantic, whose center consisted of little more than the tidy brick post office, the Congregational church, a score of houses, and an outdoor pay phone mounted on a sturdy post, moved through the day at its usual leisurely but industrious pace.

About the only person in the community who took analytical notice of the weather was Charley Grocé. Husky and rugged, he was a Mennonite, the Pennsylvania German sect that held the same beliefs as the Amish but accepted the modern world with few reservations—even fewer than the Beachy Amish. And the Mennonites worshiped in churches rather than in homes.

But Grocé was an anomaly in other ways. His roots were not German, but Spanish. He was a free-lance photographer for the Pennsylvania Game Commission, was in the process of preparing an exhibit of his works, a one-man show at Carnegie-Mellon in Pittsburgh. He had grown up as a Catholic in parts of New Mexico and Texas, where he had lived through three hefty tornadoes. He married a Mennonite girl from Atlantic and moved back with her to convert to her church. His conversion was difficult. But soon he became a leader as the regional representative of the Mennonite Disaster Service, an international organization of measurable accomplishment and high respect.

Grocé stepped out on the porch of his home four miles away from Atlantic at 10:00 A.M. on May 31 and smelled something brewing in the air. Perhaps it was the memories of those three vicious twisters in Texas. "The humidity is so high you can cut it with a knife," he said to himself, "but I doubt if anyone will pay any attention." He went back into his house and turned on WKBS in Youngstown. The reports said nothing about tornadoes, but they underlined the severe-weather possibilities originating from the early-morning Kansas City dispatches. He refused to let himself get alarmed about the possibility. The only thing he could do was to wait and see. He would not have long to wait.

3. / *A ROW OF DUCKPINS*

The region that embraces eastern Ohio and western Pennsylvania is monitored by two flagship weather stations, in Cleveland and Pittsburgh. They are known officially as National Weather Service forecast offices. Satellite stations are in Youngstown and Erie, among others, each responsible for specific counties in their areas. The local forecasts are synchronized with the National Severe Storms Forecast Center in Kansas City.

It is the responsibility of Kansas City to issue severe thunderstorm and tornado *watches* for anywhere in the country. The local stations are responsible for fanning out the information to the key disaster services. These would bear the brunt of the ravages of the weather on the people and towns that were stricken. The local weather stations also have another important responsibility: It is up to them to decide if a severe storm or tornado *warning* should be issued.

There is a clear distinction between a "watch" and a "warning." Much of the public is unaware of it, especially where severe weather is not common. Both words sound similar. Sometimes they are inverted in the public mind. The National Weather Service makes intense efforts to get the distinction across. Because of public indifference, it is not always successful. The failure to understand the difference between the words can sometimes be disastrous.

A tornado *watch* means simply that conditions are ripe for tornadoes in a given area, but the exact locations cannot be defined. A watch is issued very sparingly, because people tire easily of false alarms. They will pay little or no attention to them if they come too frequently. Further, the watch area usually can cover a surface of some twenty-five thousand square miles. Here, tornadoes probably lurk deep inside the storm cells. The situation the forecasters face is like that in which a pipe bomb is remotely suspected somewhere within several hundred city blocks. The question is: Should a total evacuation be called for?

A tornado *warning* is issued locally under even more stringent conditions. Warnings usually are not issued except under two conditions. The first is when a report comes in that a twister has been sighted by a responsible spotter or observer on the ground—the "ground truth," in other words. The second is when what is called a hook echo is observed on a weather station radar. These are not always reliable in the present state of the art. In spite of all the modern electronic and satellite scientific wizardry, the National Weather Service still has to rely mainly on the human eye for the final devastating threat that a tornado carries with it.

This might mean a matter of seconds before scrambling for safety to the cellar. But every second counts when it means getting down a flight of cellar stairs. This is the best and sometimes only defense against a three-hundred-mile-an-hour wind and the shrapnel of debris a single tornado can catapult through the air. This can include anything from telephone poles to freight cars to cattle—to human bodies. The concentrated violence of a tornado can make the hundred-mile-an-hour winds of a hurricane seem pale. It is the difference between a rocket and grapeshot.

This is the situation the meteorologists faced on May 31. The vacillation of the weather made the job doubly difficult—a psychological climate for the forecasters of frustration and doubt. At the Youngstown National Weather Service office, halfway between Cleveland and Pittsburgh and sixty miles from each, the same problems existed: uncertainty and puzzlement about what *should* be happening in the weather but wasn't.

Among the towns the Youngstown station was responsible for were Newton Falls, Ohio, with a population of some five thousand, and Niles, Ohio, with some twenty thousand. Because of its proximity to the Pennsylvania border, the Youngstown weather office also covered the small industrial town of Wheatland in that neighboring state. Whatever was to happen, at least Youngstown provided a vital link between the two weather flagship stations in Cleveland and Pittsburgh to forewarn the population in its jurisdiction in case of a tornado watch or warning.

The three towns—Newton Falls, Niles, and Wheatland—under the wing of the Youngstown weather station are strung in an east-to-west line just to the north of U.S. 76 in Ohio, which continues eastward as U.S. 80. The towns are a handful of miles apart from each other. The first two towns were vintage settlements of the Connecticut Western Reserve and were founded roughly a century after the grant on the cusp of the early 1800s. There is the faint suggestion of Connecticut influence still remaining in a few of the white clapboard houses scattered about and in the shady maples arching the roads. Downtown, the brick and stone buildings reflect the Victorian days and the industrial revolution, with somber brick and stone buildings framing the main street. Elsewhere, the twentieth century takes over, with clusters of ranch houses and the inevitable Rotary and Kiwanis signs heralding the regular weekly meetings of the clubs. On May 31 there were several highlights in the offing for several of the residents.

In Newton Falls, Betsy Atkins, wheelchaired with a broken leg, looked forward with a hundred or so of her congenial women companions to the regular bingo game to be held in the American Legion Hall in the town's center at six o'clock that evening.

At the First Church of God, an imposing brick edifice on Broad Street, the Reverend Dr. Lillie McCutcheon was planning her house and hospital calls at the parsonage next to the church, and preparing for her Sunday worship. On the church schedule that evening was a happy event: the small family wedding for Diane and Ronald Taylor, relatives of apprentice pastor Bob Benak. It would be held in the small chapel of the church, and the usual euphoria was high.

Dr. McCutcheon was a woman of quiet strength, a firm believer that God can do anything. She dedicated her life and her mission to proving that premise. Her church was an ample structure of uncertain but spacious modern architecture, with two chapels in addition to the main church. With her husband, she conducted what they called an outreach ministry by faith to meet human needs and share the gospel. Both were devout born-again Christians with a firm belief in divine healing. The congregation was enthusiastic. They came to the services by the busload.

Elsewhere in Newton Falls, the town was going about its usual business, some of it slack because of the economic slowdown. Clayton Reakes was lucky. His own company, the Trumbull Pattern Works, was able to keep busy. He also kept busy in other things. For twenty-one years he had been an officer of the Newton Falls Public Safety Reserve. He took the job seriously, assisting the police and fire departments with all sorts of emergencies. Sometimes he was kidded for his enthusiasm. Over the years he had laboriously climbed up the iron rungs to the roof of the Municipal Hall to scan the horizon for tornadoes at the first sign of a tornado watch issued by the National Weather Service. Most of the time it was wasted energy; the threat never developed. Some of his friends counted that he had responded to twenty-three false alarms. However, on the morning of May 31, Reakes sensed something in the air. He made sure he was within range of his scanner and tuned his radio to the NOAA weather reports. Not that he expected heavy weather. But if some were brewing, he'd be ready for it in spite of the ribbing from his friends.

His lieutenant in the Public Safety Reserve, Larry Sembach, also was conscientious. He worked in the engineering department of the telephone company in a nearby town. From there the weather gave no special concern. There was nothing but bright, sunlit sky. But like Reakes, he never let down his guard too much. He took any severe-weather watch as seriously as a warning. Both were in the minority.

*   *   *

In Niles, barely ten miles to the east, the day was normal enough. Much of the activity took place on "the strip," that traffic-jammed four-lane sort of highway that all through America merges one town with another without a change in the nature or ambience, without a borderline to be discerned. In Niles, it was U.S. 422. As in nearly every other bustling American town, there was the Pizza Hut, Burger King, Mr. Donut, Dunkin' Donuts, McDonald's, and a half dozen auto dealers with long lines of gold or silver foil whipping in the wind and strung between high, brushed-aluminum floodlight poles.

Downtown, off the strip, where local bankers, lawyers, and office workers conducted their business, the atmosphere was less brassy. Nearby was the imposing classical Greek structure in memory of President William McKinley. It looked as if it had been sliced out of Washington and transplanted in Niles, the town of his birth. Some have commented that the memorial is considerably more impressive than his accomplishments. Downtown also was the new red brick police and fire station, modern and spotless. Station Number 2, up on Vienna Road, was equally trim and smart, with spit-and-polish engines always ready to answer the sirens. The station sat across the road from the Convenience Food Mart and next to the cemetery.

The four corners where Vienna Road met U.S. 422 were particularly active. The Niles Park Plaza, a large, sprawling, L-shaped structure, was catering to a few late Friday afternoon shoppers. Aerobics classes were under way in the Finesse Studios, while several county service offices were cleaning up their work for the weekend.

Next door to the shopping plaza was the Top of the Strip Roller Skating Rink. Over 150 schoolchildren looked forward to the opening hour of the roller skating rink on Route 422 in early evening, an especially popular activity on Fridays. In the same town, Elaine Italiano, thirty-nine, a popular first-grade teacher at Taft Elementary School, was busy planning the annual faculty spring dinner to be held at Chieffo's Restaurant, also on Route 422. The strip served as a popular mecca for everyone from surrounding towns as well, with its shopping plazas, convenience stores, service stations, and restaurants. Elaine would attend the dinner with her husband, Joe, equally popular as a physical education instructor.

There also was an active schedule of Little League and softball games on the roster. Fire Chief Charley Semple was determined to put his girls' softball team through a rigorous workout for an upcoming championship playoff. Enthusiasm runs high in all sections of Ohio and Pennsylvania for the evening ball games.

The baseball syndrome was especially active in neighboring Wheatland, just over the state border. Postal carrier Dave Kostka, husky and athletic, was looking forward to playing in a game that night. Married only three weeks to his wife, Yvonne, they had recently returned from their honeymoon in Hawaii. He was pleased with the proofs of their wedding pictures, although the finished pictures had not yet come back from the photographer.

The photographer who had taken the pictures was Jeff Wimer, who also was production manager at nearby Mercer, Pennsylvania, at Mutual Network station WWIZ. On May 31 his efforts were directed toward handling the manifold chores of the small studio, where he had to wear many hats, from commercials to spot news to weather. He was paying close attention to the latter, because—like so many of the others—he was scheduled to play in a softball game; then he was to dash off to the high-school graduation ceremony of a friend of his family. Actually, he was hoping for rain because of the tight schedule. But when he went off duty at two in the afternoon, he noticed a high sky and a hazy, warm, and humid day, but no rain. He decided he had to put on his softball team uniform first and carry his dress clothes with him.

In all three towns, it was an average spring day, a slice of Americana with a mixture of its joys and foibles, its energy and its doldrums. Grant Wood could join with Norman Rockwell to portray it.

The first thing forecaster Bill Drazl (pronounced "drawl") said to his chief, Chuck Heckler, when he arrived at the Pittsburgh National Weather Service station on May 31 was, "Oh, brother."

He was studying the radar, the satellite screens, and going quickly through the synoptic maps and dispatches in his own area, as well as the Kansas City reports. The surface map showed a high temperature and dew point—the latter being the measure of how much moisture there was in the air, the moisture that could rush violently upward to form giant thunderstorms.

All the other ingredients pointed to a dangerous situation. The ground temperatures were bound to increase under the afternoon sun. A very unstable atmosphere was extant. There was destabilizing cold air aloft, at twenty thousand feet. There was dry air at the midlevels. Something was bound to happen. The soundings from Pittsburgh's own weather balloon station spelled the vertical picture out. They indicated an inversion at two thousand feet that would act like putting a lid on a pot to trap the boiling water. The temperature also was doing some crazy things. At eighteen thousand feet, it had cooled off forty degrees more than expected.

Drazl's experience told him that you've got to know when to worry, and today was one of those days. But as the other station forecasters in the region noticed, nothing seemed to be developing locally as it should be as the day wore on.

The whole fan-out system to the local public was at least ready, if needed: immediate computer printouts to the teletype printers on the weather wire circuits. The Associated Press, radio and TV stations, utilities, the highway department, and the state police would pick up the watch or warning immediately. The NOAA weather radio, of course, would simultaneously dispatch the same information, preceded by a tone signal. Fire departments, EMTs, and police and county officials would pick that up, along with PEMA, the Pennsylvania Emergency Management Agency, which would further alert others. Instructions to the public would be issued via standard wording at the actual warning stage for all the units to pass along:

IF THREATENING WEATHER APPROACHES . . . GO TO A SAFE PLACE IMMEDIATELY. PROTECT YOUR HEAD. STAY AWAY FROM WINDOWS . . . DOORS . . . AND

OUTSIDE WALLS . . . CALL NATIONAL WEATHER SER-
VICE AT AREA CODE 412-644-2888.

This was the prescribed routine. It had its loopholes. The National Weather Service was trying to improve it for the future.
But future improvements were expensive and slow to develop in
the face of national budget cutbacks. On May 31, 1985, however, this was the best that could be done. And there remained
another serious problem: public indifference and apathy as far as
watches and warnings were concerned. Many still were confused
about which was which—or even realized that a tornado was the
most devastating force in all of meteorology.

Northwest of Pittsburgh and just south of the Pennsylvania
Turnpike is Beaver Falls, settled along an Indian trail in 1793
but not declared a city until 1930. It is the companion city to
North Sewickley, a bedroom town just across the Beaver River.
Chinaware is an important industrial product of the area, along
with steel and steel products. Both towns sit in a steep wooded
valley formed by the river, rugged country that had been a severe
challenge for the fragile Conestoga wagons and stagecoaches of
the past.

On Route 18, the Big Beaver Shopping Plaza was having a
busy day on Friday, May 31, with the weekend coming up. The
plaza sprawled across a wide expanse of concrete parking spaces
for over a hundred cars, framed by Jamis Motors and the Big
Beaver Restaurant on each side. The shopping center housed a
large Jamesway Department Store, a Revco Drug Store, a Comet
Food Store, a hair stylist, a body-building gym, and other enter-
prises, including a Pennsylvania State liquor store. Across the
busy traffic on Route 18 was a Sunoco station.

At the state liquor store, Carl Mosketti, a jovial man with a
handlebar moustache, was filling orders for customers looking
forward to their weekend libations. Mosketti was anticipating a
relaxing holiday himself as one of the pilot members of the Cameo
Flying Club. At the spacious Jamesway Department Store, which
sold everything from cosmetics to dresses to appliances, custom-

ers were moving through the aisles and showcases, carefully pricing the merchandise because times were not too good in the area, where smokestack industries were wilting. Jess Megaree, of Lancaster, Pennsylvania, was visiting at a relative's home for an upcoming wedding. His father-in-law would be arriving late afternoon and had instructions to call him from the Jamesway store so that Megaree could meet him there and guide him to the house.

Across the Beaver River in North Sewickley, volunteer Fire Chief Dale Sutherland, a metallurgist with the local Babcock & Wilcox tube plant, had a light day in mind. The only thing of note was that his son Dan was planning to go to an unusual graduation party that evening. It would be celebrated at the Spotlight 88 drive-in theater at the intersection of Routes 65 and 588. The outdoor drive-in shared the four corners of the busy intersection with Kemp's Butcher Shop, Hummel's Service Station, and J & J Supply, a hardware store.

A few miles to the east sits the village of Evans City. It is a trim rural town where the Rotary Club meets every Tuesday at six-fifteen and where its old drummers' hotel is freshly painted gray with clean white trim and features steaks, chops, and seafood under its mansard roof. Nearby is Joe-Dee's Pizza, which heralds both pizzas and hoagies. There is, of course, the classic corner drugstore and the inevitable railroad tracks that run close to town.

A few miles out of town at the top of a hill that commands a sweeping view of the countryside is John's Bar and Grill. It is a trim, neat building, low-slung with dark brown-stained sheathing. It houses an ample oval-shaped bar, with a family restaurant discreetly set off in a large dining room in the rear. The establishment was busy preparing for its usual bustling Friday night business.

Albion, Atlantic, Wheatland, and Beaver Falls form a north–south line parallel to the edge of the Ohio-Pennsylvania border. The line is intersected halfway down by the east–west line drawn through Newton Falls and Niles in Ohio that crosses the border to Wheatland. It made an interesting geographic alignment. In common was that all the communities were included in the neat box drawn by Steve Weiss on the weather charts of

41

Kansas City that marked the danger zone for the heavy artillery of supercell thunderheads that were bound to form and advance ahead of the cold front on their way to collide with the warm air mass coming up from the Gulf. The towns, in fact, sat ominously like duckpins. The only question the forecasters had was: Why weren't the monsters showing up on the screens?

4. / WATCH OR WARNING?

The satellite pictures coming in throughout the day at the National Severe Storms Forecast Center at the Federal Building in Kansas City clearly showed the state boundaries of the target area in overlay as perforated lines, even though Beaver Falls and the rest of the counties and towns under surveillance were of course not visible. The cold-front army that was on its way to meeting the sluggish warm front was evidenced by the clouds ahead of, along, and behind it. But they still weren't showing up where all the signs pointed they should be: in eastern Ohio and western Pennsylvania. The image also revealed a marked drying behind the cold front. It clearly appeared that the deep low-pressure system moving across the upper Great Lakes was about to pull the moisture-loaded air mass from the Gulf northward. This in turn would be bound to fuel development of giant, severe thunderstorms at any moment.

Chief Fred Ostby and forecaster Steve Weiss studied the situation intensely. The magic-eye picture from the satellite would be showing all the major phenomena, from rapidly developing thunderstorms to merging cells to intersecting boundaries. To intensify the analysis, Weiss instituted a process known as RISOP—

Rapid Interval Scan Operation—to catch more frequent cloud movement. There still was no sign of the usual clues for dangerous conditions—the giant cumulonimbus or towering cumulus clouds—where by all rights they should be developing.

But by 2:00 P.M., severe thunderstorms were smacking hard at Ontario. These would bear close watching. The possibility of the storms moving southward toward the U.S. border was very real. A whole string of weather stations in the area were scanning the situation along with Weiss and Ostby: Cleveland, Buffalo, Albany, Philadelphia, and Pittsburgh. Steve Weiss fielded their phone calls from his desk. All of them showed concern as well as puzzlement. Buffalo wanted to know if it looked as if a severe-weather watch was going to be issued. Weiss told them that since the surface pressure was falling mainly over Ontario, it probably would be best to hold up issuing a watch. He would make a direct phone call if a watch looked likely.

Philadelphia called in midafternoon. Weiss reassured them that the primary severe threat for Pennsylvania would be in the western part of the state.

When Bill Drazl called from the Pittsburgh weather station, he asked Weiss, "Where the hell is this damn thing? When is it going to break? What's going on?"

Weiss, as puzzled as Drazl was, simply said, "You tell me, Bill."

Drazl chuckled, and Weiss went on. "Seriously, we're watching those heavy thunderstorms moving into Ontario. You might continue mentioning that in the afternoon zone package you're going to release soon."

Drazl agreed, and Weiss added, "For the United States, I'm still sticking to that area of eastern Ohio, western Pennsylvania, and western New York, though. If it's going to happen, I think it's going to happen there."

They hung up.

Weiss turned back to his screens. The main set of hardware that improved tornado watch verification markedly for Kansas City was called the Centralized Storm Information System. With the National Weather Service's passion for acronyms, they dubbed it CSIS. Installed in 1982, it provided a new tool to make optimal use of remote sensing information.

Essentially, the system can assimilate on one screen what previously had to be done in the forecaster's crowded mind. Equipment consists of a GOES satellite receiving antenna, four Harris/6 computers, the output from a 604 data circuit, and two auto dialers that provide time access to radar data. The system can produce pressure, temperature, and dew-point analyses to give clues about critical vertical air currents. With the ability to locate exact points on the satellite imagery, the forecaster is provided with coordinates to locate any town in the country, from Painted Post, New York, to Tuba City, Arizona. Like magic, the system also can display radar data, and the Kansas City forecaster can interrogate any of the sixty National Weather Service radars spread across the country.

Steve Weiss had been manipulating all this electronic wizardry on May 31. He pulled in a Kavouras radar display on the CSIS from Buffalo and Pittsburgh. Buffalo was able to discern the threatening squall line in southern Ontario. But no significant precipitation showed up on the Pittsburgh screen at all. The scope was practically clear.

The same was true at the Erie weather station. And at Cleveland. And Youngstown, Buffalo, and Albany. Everyone was still continuing to look for something that seemed sure to happen but wasn't.

At Cleveland, Marvin Miller and Jack May, along with volunteer Jerry Murphy, based their relaxed mood on the climatological fact that it was very rare for tornadoes to hit Ohio in its far eastern region. When they did, the central and western parts of the state nearly always got pummeled first. Still, they kept their eyes glued to the radar screen, where only the tiny pinpoint of a shower was showing up. Close to 4:00 P.M., another small shower joined it. This was not too alarming; it was a common occurrence. They also were aware that the ground clutter around the Cleveland area made it difficult to capture storm activity aloft in the immediate vicinity. They were still not fully convinced that everything was going to clear up. Mid-springtime always was full of surprises. Even though they often joked about Canada being blamed for everything wrong with the weather, there still was that Canadian cold air hovering over the region, and that could pull an unpleasant surprise. There also was that low-level jet stream. The problem was that it was now difficult to believe that a strong enough trigger could be capable of starting a major catastrophic attack within the next hour, or even within the next day.

Experience, however, taught them to keep their eyes on the radar in this type of situation. And they did. One reason was that they were sure that if something was going to break, it would break big.

Somewhat concerned that the ground clutter of the Cleveland buildings might be masking the full picture, Jack May looked out the window shortly after 4:00 P.M. There he could see a line of storms just beginning to develop. The ominous anvil on the top of the great cumulonimbus clouds was just starting to sweep forward with its flat, overhanging top. Then the whole mass of clouds began to form a churning line. It blossomed and seemed to explode.

East of Cleveland and over the border in Pennsylvania, the staff of forecasters at the Erie airport were still as puzzled as their colleagues in Cleveland. They were punching up the graphics and printouts of their computer and interrogating the skies with their radar. At about 3:30 P.M., a few more minor thunderstorms began to pop up. But they were still in Ontario. Dave Bell manned the radar, scanning the cells horizontally, then vertically, picking up the precipitation in them but not finding any sign of a hook echo. It was still sunny in Erie, but there was a mass of clouds to the south that suddenly were picking up momentum in addition to the Ontario storms, which were without doubt backbreakers.

Usually the severe storms started in western Ohio, and were easy to track as they crossed the Ohio border into Pennsylvania. There was plenty of lead time under normal conditions. On this day there was none. Without warning, the cumulonimbus supercells grew into great clusters and formed a squall line that stretched nearly a hundred miles along the Ohio border. It was sudden and it was explosive. The Erie weather station had never seen anything quite like it.

At the Pittsburgh weather station, Chuck Heckler and Bill Drazl were continuing their vigil at the radar screen, still puzzled that nothing was coming up. It was nearing 4:00 P.M. The lack of storm development under such a threatening combination of conditions was unprecedented in their past experience, and Drazl turned to Heckler and said, "What do you counsel in a case like this, Chuck?"

"About the only thing I can counsel at this time, Bill, is patience."

At just about that time, Drazl picked up something interesting far to the north, between Cleveland and Erie. There was an extremely intense supercell moving eastward there. "Look at the return we're getting on this," Drazl said.

Heckler nodded. "Hard to believe we're picking it up at this distance."

At the Youngstown airport, the day-shift forecaster was getting ready to leave as Heckler and Drazl were making their observations in Pittsburgh. With no storms in sight, there was little reason to stay later. But a final look at the data brought an abrupt change of mind. There were some beauties springing up seemingly out of nowhere, just to the west of the Youngstown area.

Strange things were happening in the Ohio and Pennsylvania skies, and every weather station in the region suddenly was galvanized into action.

It was at 3:52 P.M. Eastern Daylight Time that Steve Weiss took a long look at the overall radar imagery he had pulled in from half a dozen stations to the east. Suddenly, everything was burgeoning just east of Cleveland, near the Pennsylvania border. It was unbelievable. Towering cumulus clouds were springing up like cancer cells. "There was suddenly a line of supercells merging like army divisions," said one forecaster who liked to mix metaphors. "The radar screen looked like measles."

Weiss made his promised telephone call to Buffalo. He was

cautious, as he had to be. He indicated that a severe-weather watch would be needed soon. But he wanted to examine more information, especially if the watch would include the tornado possibility. Then he would call back.

A warning, as opposed to a watch, would be issued only by the local stations. They could monitor their close-in territories more accurately than Kansas City. An official warning usually is not issued without an actual sighting on the ground—the "ground truth." A warning also was advisable if that hook echo was discernible on the local radar screen, although sometimes these curly fishhook images indicated that the twister was already on the ground.

Weiss turned back to the screen. He was shocked to see how fast the supercells were bursting on the scene and pockmarking the image.

The moment of truth had just about arrived, that moment when the agonizing decision had to be made. The weathermen did not like to be alarmists. They also hated to fail to make a decision that might save many lives. There was a delicate balance between the two.

At 4:15 P.M., Weiss called Marvin Miller in Cleveland. Miller confirmed that the western point of the frontal attack was now near Akron on his scope and moving eastward fast.

"We're just about set to issue a tornado watch," he told Miller.

"Not just a severe-thunderstorm watch, right?" Miller said. "Are we going for tornadoes?"

"We've got that strong wind field and those mighty powerful supercells moving in. Plus all the other signs."

"Yup," said Miller. "It sure looks good to me, too."

Neither Miller nor the other stations in the target area disagreed.

At 4:25 P.M. Eastern Daylight Time, Weiss again slid his chair over to the CSIS keyboard and typed out Tornado Watch Number 211:

BULLETIN—IMMEDIATE BROADCAST REQUESTED
TORNADO WATCH NUMBER 211
4:25 PM EDT FRI MAY 31 1985

A . . . THE NATIONAL SEVERE STORMS FORECAST
CENTER HAS ISSUED A TORNADO WATCH FOR
PORTIONS OF EASTERN OHIO
PORTIONS OF THE NORTHERN PANHANDLE, W.
VA.
PORTIONS OF WESTERN PENNSYLVANIA
PARTS OF SOUTHWEST NEW YORK
PORTIONS OF CENTRAL AND EASTERN LAKE ERIE
SOUTHERN LAKE ONTARIO
FROM 500 PM EDT UNTIL 1100 PM THIS FRIDAY AF-
TERNOON AND EVENING.

B . . . TORNADOES . . . LARGE HAIL . . . DANGEROUS
LIGHTNING AND DAMAGING THUNDERSTORM WINDS
ARE POSSIBLE IN THESE AREAS.
THE TORNADO WATCH AREA IS ALONG AND 70
STATUTE MILES NORTH AND SOUTH OF A LINE 20 MILES
SOUTHWEST OF AKRON OHIO TO 20 MILES SOUTH OF
ROCHESTER NEW YORK.
REMEMBER . . . A TORNADO WATCH MEANS CONDI-
TIONS ARE FAVORABLE FOR TORNADOES AND SEVERE
THUNDERSTORMS IN AND CLOSE TO THE WATCH AREA.
PERSONS IN THESE AREAS SHOULD BE ON THE LOOK-
OUT FOR THREATENING WEATHER CONDITIONS AND
LISTEN FOR LATER STATEMENTS AND POSSIBLE
WARNINGS.
. . .WEISS

As Weiss was tapping out the message at 4:25 P.M., Linda
Quay was in her kitchen in Albion, Pennsylvania, hundreds of
miles to the east. With her three children and a neighboring child
scampering around her, she was taking a platter of haddock out
of the refrigerator and getting ready to cook it for supper. Sandra
Stahlsmith, a few blocks away, was going through the same sort
of routine. She was preparing some hard-boiled eggs for the
school lunches the next day. Neither had yet noticed anything
special about the weather.

Bob McClymond, the editor of the *Albion News,* was in the one-
story white stucco news office, putting the next edition to bed.

John Halfast, the Erie staff weather forecaster, had already said
good-bye to his wife and left his home in Albion to report for
work at the weather office at the Erie airport.

Gene Hart, the Pennsylvania State Park assistant superintendent at Pymatuning, was closing up his office and preparing to drive his truck through the forest to his home on the park grounds.

In Atlantic, Pennsylvania, Ammon Miller was back on his Amish farm, doing some light welding on a metal brace. Elderly Andy Byler was finishing up his light chores in the barn of his farm, while Bishop Ed Yoder still was working away from home, helping to build his friend's house. Reverend Polley of the Atlantic Congregational Church was in nearby Meadville, helping his son put a deck on a house. Many of the clergy of any sect or denomination in the area had calluses on the palms of their hands from manual work during the week.

In the other towns in both Ohio and Pennsylvania that had been defined as tornado watch areas, the routine was much the same. People were winding up the week as in any other week, whether it was Public Safety Reserve Clayton Reakes, Reverend McCutcheon, or Betsy Atkins in Newton Falls, or schoolteacher Elaine Italiano or Fire Chief Charley Semple, all in Ohio; or softball enthusiasts Dave Kostka and Jeff Wimer, just over the border from the others in the Wheatland, Pennsylvania, area. Beaver Falls, too, just below them, was in a weekend mood, and the Big Beaver Shopping Plaza was filled with parked cars and energetic shoppers.

Very few were paying any attention to the weather, which still remained benign to local eyes, except for the oppressive and stifling heat. Very few, if any, were yet aware of what was going on behind the scenes in the weather stations as far away as Kansas City and as near as Cleveland, Youngstown, Erie, and Pittsburgh.

5. /DEADLY HARBINGER

The supercells that were exploding so ruthlessly on the local radar screens were the spawning grounds of tornadoes. Inside the violent updrafts and downdrafts, the fetuses of twisters lurk, invisible before they strike with the most devastating power in weather. Over a fifty-year span, tornadoes have killed as many people as all the floods and hurricanes in the country combined. They burst out of hiding so quickly there is rarely time for an effective warning. They can stay on the ground from a few seconds to more than three hours. The swath of destruction can range from a few feet to over two miles in width. The murderous path can run from a few feet long to over two hundred miles. The wind speeds inside the funnel can rage at over three hundred miles an hour.

No direct measurements have ever been made. Any instrument yet designed would be obliterated by the winds it was trying to measure. Most sinister is that tornadoes can come in families, one following another, striking different paths across cities, towns, and countryside.

All day long, Ostby, Weiss, and their fellow meteorologists in Kansas City kept probing for the key signals that might brew tornadoes. The warm, moist air was a critical parameter. On the ground, many of the citizens of Newton Falls, Wheatland, Albion, or the other towns already had noticed the key preamble: the sultry and muggy air pulled in from the Gulf of Mexico. The warm, dry air at the low to middle layers of the atmosphere was another foreboding sign, while the cold and dry air of the upper level joined with the bad omens of the day.

Important also in the computations of the National Severe Storms Forecast Center was the low pressure in the middle and upper layers moving from west to east. These regions were called troughs, causing the air to rise in front of them, joined by the effect of the swift jet stream. Then there was the heat from the afternoon sun. It baked the ground, bulldozing the warm surface air upward, forcing it to rise like a hot-air balloon, releasing more heat as the lifted air condensed. These were the kinds of parameters that enabled Weiss and Ostby to predict the possibility of tornadoes before the storms had even begun to form and still remained invisible.

No region suffers as many tornadoes as the continental United States. Such frequency is unheard of anywhere else in the world. Average number per year: 700. Average fatalities: 94 each year. Total tornadoes since 1916: 26,742. "Tornado Alley" in the Great Plains gets pummeled the most. But the deadliest, bringing the most concentrated fatalities, hit the heavily populated East and Southeast where least expected, and warnings and watches are more often ignored.

When the white narrow spinning funnel of a tornado strikes, it may quickly turn black and dirty, and widen as it swells with debris sucked up in the tube. Other debris spins around the outside of the funnel that from a distance may look like carrions circling a corpse. From a close view, the "birds" turn out to be rooftops, beams, planks, animals, or trucks blackened by mud and dirt.

Tornadoes have been described by dozens of other metaphors: writhing snakes, angry elephant trunks, undulating ropes, unstoppable hoses that suck upward like an enormous vacuum cleaner, a drill press with multiple high-speed bits, or a giant rotary mower leaving a path that swirls like an equally giant Slinky. The sound, the roar is constantly described as ''indescribable''—except that the phrase ''a thousand express trains'' is constantly repeated.

The supercell thunderstorms that bring all this havoc soar up to twelve miles in the atmosphere. Not content to breed tornadoes alone, they lash out with blustering gust fronts and surface winds, and plaster the ground with vicious hail up to the size of baseballs and even grapefruit. The intense updrafts of the supercells are lethal. They can rise like an elevator, lifting at speeds of a hundred miles an hour or more, holding the heavy hail and rain aloft like Ping-Pong balls.

The huge cumulonimbus cloud with a lowered, rain-free base usually moves to the northeast, as a strong southwest jet stream carries the rain and hail away from the updraft and lets it dump its freezing and liquid cargo on the earth. The hail, heavier than the rain, reaches the ground first, smashing crops, pocking metal surfaces, bruising animals and people.

The strong winds aloft bring in dry air. It is cooled by evaporation as it swirls around the updraft. This air begins to sink in the form of monumental downdrafts. Then a circulation develops. A viciously rotating motion sets in, like an ice skater spinning with arms akimbo. The rising air of the updraft begins to curve counterclockwise high in the main storm tower. The descending downdraft air does the same. This swirling five- or ten-mile-wide motion goes into action as high as twenty-five thousand feet above the ground. The beginning of the much smaller but more intense tornado vortex begins to form. It spins faster with ever-increasing momentum, like the ice skater now pulling in his arms to increase the spin. The funnel may take up to an hour to reach the ground—or it may not reach the ground at all.

High at the top of the towering supercell, the flat anvil head sweeps forward of the main cloud. What is called an overshooting top bulges as much as several thousand feet above the anvil, where the updraft reaches its greatest height. Some may show up at the top of the cloud like a bubble bursting through a boiling pan of porridge. Just beneath the anvil, an ugly, dark mammatus cloud layer spreads out, an ominous cloud bulging with hundreds of udders, a sign along with hail of possible tornadoes. But neither one is a cause of them.

At the rain-free base of the supercell, a small rotating "wall" cloud often forms, roughly fifteen hundred feet above the ground. This is most frequently the springboard from which the tornado makes its lethal plunge to the earth—the screaming whirlwind whose roots have begun high up in the supercell. When the tornado is ready to strike, condensation caused by lowered atmospheric pressure makes the funnel visible to the eye. The lowered pressure also creates the unmeasurable suction within.

Because tornadoes strike almost as unpredictably as lightning, forecasters remain frustrated by their present-day "watch" and "warning" system. Current radar in use at National Weather Service stations can detect the precipitation hidden inside the supercell. But it cannot detect the direction or speed of the wind within the cell. Without that capacity the ordinary radar cannot determine the whirling circulation that creates the tornado. The more recent Doppler radar can catch most of that motion, a giant step forward. However, the deployment of planned Doppler-computer systems lies several years in the future. And neither radar system can reach beyond 140 miles.

Fred Ostby, along with several others at the Kansas City center, was an avid student of tornadoes. Among other outbreaks, he had made a detailed study of a family of violent tornadoes that hit Ruskin Heights, a Kansas City, Missouri, suburb, on May 20, 1957. It reflected a striking example of how weather patterns develop to create the conditions ripe for tornado devastation. At nine in the morning that day, a weather system lay west and south of Kansas City. There were strong, low-level winds. A warm front lay across southwestern Kansas and Oklahoma. The winds began shoving the warm, moist air to the northeast, toward Kansas City. To the west was a flow of warm, dry air coming in from the desert to the southwest. High aloft, as Ostby noted in his study, the jet stream winds raced in gentle curves on their east-to-west express route. All the ingredients formed a perfect scenario for a smashing outbreak of severe weather, especially since the sun warmed the surface and low-level air more as the day wore on.

Like a pot of soup with a flame under it, the warm air rose. Its destiny could only be a clash with the upper air disturbance. By

11:00 A.M. the first tornado of the day smashed into eastern Colorado. In the afternoon, severe thunderstorms with bellies full of tornadoes spread across southern Nebraska and northern Kansas. They were most severe where the upper jet stream cut across the advancing warm front, creating a moving zone of concentrated weather mayhem. The whole package approached Kansas City at about 6:00 P.M.

Meanwhile, another pack of tornadoes sprang to life at about 5:00 P.M. in northeastern Oklahoma, ahead of the advancing dry air. The havoc raged for nearly six hours, adding up to a total of thirty-five tornadoes.

But the Kansas City suburb of Ruskin Heights was destined for the major blow. The severe-weather forecaster on duty in Kansas City could see it coming. In late morning he put out a tornado watch that defined a neat rectangle in the general area. In mid- and late afternoon, two more tornado watches were issued. They included Kansas City and surroundings. A lot of people were now ready for it.

The big killer tornado swept on a line from the southwest toward the northeast, moving across the ground at nearly fifty miles an hour. Tornado warnings spread quickly ahead of it. Volunteer storm spotters saw it. They called radio and TV stations. It was easy to see over the great wide plains of Kansas as it raced toward the Missouri line. It was black and thick and ugly, a third of a mile wide. At times it split into multiple vortexes, whirling around each other like angry dervishes. By the time it approached Ruskin Heights, its devastating track was nearly seventy miles long. It roared down on the suburban houses and smashed them like a balsa wood village hit by a high-powered vacuum cleaner.

Thirty-seven people were killed. The consensus was that many scores more would have died without the numerous tornado watches and warnings.

Ostby had made dozens of tornado analyses of this sort over the years. They reinforced his dedication to the importance of watches and warnings—and the critical role played by the volunteer spotters and ham radio operators in the face of the unstoppable fury of both tornadoes and severe thunderstorms as well. That "ground truth" was the final link in man's struggle against the most vicious and elusive phenomenon of meteorology. Even when the future network of Doppler radar would be available, it would not provide the whole answer.

The volunteer spotters were trained to recognize the forewarnings. Heavy lightning, of course, was an important precursor, although it was not always present. The time between the lightning flash and the sound of thunder was another clue the spotter was trained to look for. Thunder is the sound produced by expansion of air heated by the high-amperage lightning stroke. When they come together like a cannon shot, the bolt is right in the area. Otherwise, the distance in miles to a lightning flash could be estimated by counting the number of seconds between the lightning and thunder and dividing by five.

Hail also was important to check. The size of the hailstones was an important indicator of thunderstorm intensity. Spotters of the Skywarn system were requested to report all hailstones more than a quarter inch in diameter.

But all these factors were only precursors of the actual tornado—and some of them might not be present at all. The spotters had been trained to look and listen for specific details once an actual tornado watch had been issued. Aside from the partial success of the radar hook echo, the weather stations were reluctant to issue that actual warning until a spotter report came in.

A good spotter would look for any protuberance or rotary motion at the base of a thundercloud system. Some of these protuberances were deceptive. The rain column of a thundershower might appear as a dark, solid base between a black cloud and the ground, but a tornado appendage would be narrower and more distinctly outlined.

Thunderstorms often generate a bewildering display of shapes and patterns that look suspiciously like tornadoes but are not. Some rainfalls or snowfalls from a cloud evaporate before reaching the ground. Sometimes it suggests a V-shape but is slow-moving. The real tornado funnel displays rapidly twisting particles whirling about the funnel cloud. Some accessory clouds form along the base of heavy thunderstorms, like a roll cloud or a shelf cloud. They look ominous, but the so-called wall cloud that spits out a tornado is attached to the thunder cell. All this makes it easy to confuse the real with the false. What the spotter had to discern was the twisting motion around a vertical axis. This was the basic clue in separating the real from the relatively harmless. The violence of the twisting motion was another clue. And even then such a pattern was not considered a full tornado until it touched the ground.

There was another subtlety for the ground observer to look for: a rotating cloud of debris on the ground itself, without a visible funnel coming down from the cloud. These are the invisible whirlwinds. They are seen only when a violently spinning column of air formed in the cloud begins to pick up debris and dust from the ground. The longer this ghostlike form of tornado stays on the ground, the darker it becomes. The debris is actually lifted up toward the cloud.

Then, of course, there's the sound. The eerie and unmistakable roar often can be heard several miles away. It grows louder as the funnel approaches the ground. It becomes loudest when it moves across the surface.

Through the efforts of the National Weather Service, the Skywarn network has become an integral link in the chain of defense against tornadoes. Their instructions as to what to do are specific: Telephone severe-weather observations immediately to the National Weather Service or alternate agency, collect if necessary; instruct the operator that it is an emergency call. Otherwise, they are to notify law-enforcement, Civil Defense, or fire-department agencies. The message should be brief: what was seen, where it was seen, when it was seen, what it was doing when seen.

It was hard to judge the intensity. That could be done only after the tornado had done its worst. A scientist at the University of Chicago, T. Theodore Fujita, is credited with establishing the tornado scale that bears his name.

He has devoted his life to the study of tornadoes. "Tornadoes are like criminals who cannot get away without leaving their fingerprints," he once told a reporter. "But I love them. I think I've reached the point of no return. I've almost forgotten why I am doing this. It has become a passion."

Fujita uses dry ice and suction fans to produce miniature tornadoes, and he has tracked more than 250 tornadoes covering two
thousand miles of the ugly tracks that tornadoes leave in their
wakes. In doing so, he has established the Fujita scale, which
runs from F-0 to F-5 in measuring the intensity.

Winds of F-0 tornadoes range from 40 to 72 miles an hour;
light damage may be expected. F-1 and F-2 tornadoes create
moderate to considerable damage. They rip off roofs and blast
windows out of their frames. Their winds within the funnel are
estimated at a mere 73 up to 157 miles an hour. F-3 and F-4
tornadoes range from severe to devastating damage, with winds
from 158 to 260 miles an hour. The F-5 twister creates what is
called incredible damage, with winds up to an estimated 318
miles an hour, practically three times that of a massive hurricane.
Even telephone poles and giant beams become shrapnels. Picture
a telephone pole catapulting down a river, rushing downstream at
over three hundred miles an hour—and what the resulting collision would be.

But since the winds of these violent tornadoes have never been
measured firsthand, the speed estimates are judged by what the
resulting damage has been. Some feel that speeds have been even
higher—four hundred, five hundred, even six hundred miles an
hour. Whatever the maximum, the havoc, the ghastly damage to
life, property, and Nature at times seems unmeasurable. The
strongest oak becomes a sapling. Walls of houses become cardboard. Steel beams become soda straws. Trucks and autos become accordions. Yet often trees, houses, and trucks a few feet
outside the swath remain untouched. Chickens are stripped naked
of their feathers—yet remain otherwise unharmed. Tiny straws
are embedded in trees. Planks at times do the same: plunging into
the tree trunk and sticking out like a diving board, with the
strength to hold the weight of a man.

On May 31, 1985—the peak of the annual tornado season—
about the only specific clue available to sniff out a tornado at a
distance for local weather stations in the target area of eastern
Ohio and western Pennsylvania was the ''hook'' echo on their

conventional radar screens, often but not always reliable. On the screen, this looks like the numeral 6, or a fishhook. This shows that the precipitation pattern is being wrapped around that vicious rotating column of air that just could be near the spot of a descending tornado. In addition to the ''ground truth'' of a responsible spotter, a tornado warning often is issued on this basis.

Since this hook spotted on the local radar screen can mean that the tornado already is on the ground, the dive for the cellar has a critically short fuse. Again, in this age of science, the only thing that could be fully depended on was the human eye of a reliable observer.

On May 31, all the future plans for Doppler-computer systems were on the drawing boards. Yet all the signs were suddenly pointing toward the worst: not one, but a full family of tornadoes, a multiple litter that could claw along multiple paths, multiple counties, multiple towns, and multiple homes in a territory that could reach all the way from Lake Erie to Pittsburgh and below, practically the whole length of the Pennsylvania-Ohio border.

It was not surprising, then, that one of the first palpable harbingers of trouble ahead came into the Cleveland weather station almost simultaneously with the announcement of Tornado Watch Number 211: One-inch-diameter hail was reported just east of Cleveland, in Geauga County. It smacked hard into fruit trees, vineyards, and automobiles.

6. / THE STRANGE YELLOW SKY

After Steve Weiss issued Tornado Watch Number 211 at 4:25 P.M. Eastern Daylight Time, the situation was out of Kansas City's hands, and into those of the principal local weather stations: Erie, Cleveland, Youngstown, and Pittsburgh. All were interlocked and interacting with each other. Each had its own job to do to report the tornado watch and get out severe-weather warnings, which could change to tornado warnings the minute a spotter report came in with the "ground truth," or a deadly hook showed up on local radar.

At Erie, the weather station put out a severe-thunderstorm warning at 4:30 P.M. Pittsburgh, farthest away from the wall of approaching thunder cells, flashed the tornado watch at 4:45 P.M., then joined with Erie in scanning the supercells with radar. A steady stream of warnings went out, but none of them yet upgraded for tornadoes.

The storm alerts were moving out in swift order on the whirring teletypes, the alphanumeric computer screens at the weather stations and out over the air to the public on NOAA weather radio, TV crawls, the vital amateur radio operators, fire, police, and officials, and the designated commercial Emergency Broadcasting System stations in each area.

But the big question was: Was anybody listening, paying attention? The rarity of tornadoes in eastern Ohio and western Pennsylvania created a blasé attitude: It can't happen here. Old wives' tales were extant: Tornadoes can't go over hills and rough terrain (they can); just open windows a crack to neutralize the pressure (it doesn't work); tornadoes are broken up by big buildings (they aren't); cities are immune (they're not, even though at rare times a tornado accidentally splits around a structure).

At five that evening, Albion was getting ready to close for the business day. Joe's Tavern on State Street by the railroad tracks was welcoming a few thirsty workers for a Bud Lite or two. The Zenith Radio and TV Shop was about to close up shop. The A.M.-P.M. Mini Market was tending to the convenience shopping needs of homeward-bound shoppers. The Moose Hall across the way had not begun any of its varied evening activities.

Outside of the village, in Conneaut Township, Richard Bomboy was one of the few citizens who was showing concern about the weather. Confined to a wheelchair, Bomboy made up for his limited physical activity by his volunteer work with the National Weather Service's Skywarn network. He operated with the aid of a high directional radio tower, and he kept alert for any emergency operation that might be needed. Situated between Erie and Cleveland, he could keep in touch with both weather stations.

Through the Cleveland repeater radio with its automated weather alerts, he got the word from Ohio shortly after four that severe thunderstorms were moving eastward toward the Pennsylvania border. He also knew that the weather service was extremely conservative in issuing any kind of alert. He had a videocamera on the tower with a 180-degree sweep, and he could see the towering cumulonimbus battlements approaching. As a trained spotter, he also could discern the formidable low-hanging wall cloud at the base—a frequent precursor of tornadoes. But only the tornado watch had been issued. It had not yet been upgraded to a warning.

He waited anxiously as the ominous thunder cells moved closer, keeping in touch by radio with both Cleveland and Erie. Both of them were now spilling out a flood of severe-storm warnings to most of the counties in Ohio and Pennsylvania under their coverage.

At the Cleveland office, the forecasters were working under a degraded AFOS mode, operating at a slower speed and deprived of about half the graphics on their terminal screens. Additional staff had been called in, and Skywarn's Jerry Murphy was at the ham radio desk next to the severe-weather coordinator. The latter was almost swamped with the menacing data showing up. The staffer manning the NOAA weather radio was facing the same overload, with barely enough time to get a message out before another was demanded. Another staffer was glued to the radar screen, which was bursting with threatening data. The phone desk was overloaded. Busy signals were constant. Communications with Youngstown showed signs of faltering, a crisis situation when interaction among all the region's stations was urgent.

At the Erie station, Dave Bell was manning the radar. Volunteer ham radio operator Lee Robinson had appeared just in time to carry the radio communication load. He had heard the alerts while driving home from work, and driven directly to the Erie airport. He began mobilizing all the ham radio operators he could reach. Bell continued to monitor the supercells vertically and horizontally on the radar.

Suddenly he stopped scanning. He sighted a clear hook echo. Shaped like a giant comma, it was unmistakable. At almost the same moment, a radio call came in from Bomboy. It was exactly 5:05 P.M.

"Just spotted a tornado touch-down," Bomboy said. "About five miles west of Albion. Actually, I see at least two of 'em forming. In an area called Jumbo Woods. Heading directly toward Albion."

"Check," Bell told him. "We'll get a tornado warning out right away."

Bomboy signed off. Then he got on the scanner channel to the Albion Fire Department.

Fire Chief Herk Shearer was at home. A frantic call came to

him from the fire station. Not only had Bomboy called in, but also a woman outside of town to the west had called and reported not one but three tornadoes touching down. They had hit, she said, just three miles west of the Jumbo Woods area—only a hop, skip, and jump from Albion.

Chief Shearer jumped in his truck and headed down to the town center.

Standing in front of the Albion firehouse, volunteer fireman Roger Seeley was surprised by the sudden clatter of hailstones. Out on the street, a group of kids were romping in the downburst, tossing the hailstones in the air, laughing and munching on the crusty pellets. Then, for some reason, Seeley looked up at the sky.

He saw in the distance a huge, ill-defined gray mass. It was spiraling, but it was almost transparent, like a clear liquid plastic. Inside, it appeared that a flock of birds were whirling madly in confusion. He looked closer. They were not birds. They were chunks of debris, including rooftops. The whole spinning mass seemed to be heading straight toward him. He yelled to the other firemen as they yanked the kids off the street and pushed them into the firehouse. Then they hit the fire siren.

In Jumbo Woods, affectionately called Frog Town by the residents, thirteen-year-old Tracy Petrilla was headed toward her home across a field. She looked up and saw an enormous twister coming toward her. It crashed into the woods by her house, splintering and demolishing every tree in sight. She dove for a culvert. It was half full of water. She looked up to the sky. Then she saw the twister split in two. The funnels passed her on each side, then rejoined into a single whirling mass. It appeared to be two city blocks wide. It was headed directly toward the center of Albion.

At just before five o'clock that evening, Pennsylvania State Trooper Bradley Mills had finished a tour of duty and was relaxing in front of the TV set at his home near Albion. Suddenly a crawl moved across the bottom of the screen: TORNADO WATCH IN EFFECT. . . . He went to the window and looked out. The weather had turned; it was black and gusting.

In moments a young boy ran up to his front door. He was

almost in panic. A tornado had been sighted, and he wanted to try to call his mother. He was sobbing, and he kept repeating one line over and over: "Albion's blown up! It's just blown up!" Then a beep went off on Trooper Mills's scanner. He picked up the phone to call his State Police headquarters. The line was dead.

In her living room on South Park Avenue in Albion, Linda Quay was relieved that the T-ball game had been called off on account of rain, even though five-year-old Michael wasn't happy about it. Her husband, Charley, assistant chief of the Albion Volunteer Fire Department, made the decision. They would have the haddock supper she had been planning, but in a more relaxed way. As she prepared the final touches, however, her husband's CB scanner suddenly came on the air with an alert signal. The message was brief: All firemen to the firehall at once. Charley quickly left. Linda placed little Bonnie Sue in her high chair and called for the other kids to come to the table.

At just about that time, she noticed that their dog began whimpering and cowering for no apparent reason, as if to foreshadow the enormous thunderclap that followed immediately. Ten-year-old Billy ran to turn off the TV set. As he did, all the lights went out. Since this was not uncommon during heavy storms, Linda had wall sconces ready. She began to light the candles, to the delight of the children. In spite of the threatening storm, they would at least have a nice, cozy dinner by candlelight.

At the time Linda Quay began serving her dinner, editor Bob McClymond had closed up the news office and was driving a few blocks to his home on Jackson Avenue. From the sunny weather in the afternoon, the skies darkened and his windshield was almost blotted out by sheets of rain. His windshield wipers had a hard time clearing the view ahead. But it was a warm spring rain, and the neighborhood kids were romping on nearby lawns, enjoying the break from the muggy weather of the day. His wife, Ann, was upstairs sewing, and he called to her that he was going to mix himself a Manhattan in the family room. As he did, a loud clap of thunder shook the house. He looked out the window and saw that the skies were even blacker, with an ugly yellow cast. Strange, he said to himself, this seems to be a lot more than a refreshing spring shower. He finished mixing his drink and sat down to enjoy it in spite of the weather.

Red Cross Chairman Martha Sherman arrived home at her husband's dairy farm near Albion after a routine day, and she noticed a nice, warm breeze picking up as she approached her house. Then, suddenly, the breeze died and a rather ominous still calm fell over the landscape. There also was that strange yellow sky. She walked into the living room, where her elderly mother greeted her. Then she crossed the room to turn on the TV set. She was not really surprised when a crawl appeared across the bottom of the screen. She turned on her scanner immediately. The voice of the dispatcher at the West County Communications Center came on: The tornado watch had been upgraded to a warning. All firemen were being called to the firehouse. Then all the electric power in the house went off.

In her house on the corner of Thornton and East Pearl streets, Sandra Stahlsmith, four months pregnant, looked out her window to see her sons Zachary, three, and Luke, six, outside playing in the sudden hailstorm. They were trying to catch and nibble on the golf-ball-size lumps. It was almost comical to watch them, but the wind was building up to a fury. She was tempted to let them play a little longer, but then the fire siren sounded and she started to call them into the house. Quite suddenly, she heard a neighbor call out to her that her scanner had just put out a tornado alert. She wasn't completely sure what that meant, but she yelled for the boys to get in the house, called upstairs for daughters Brook, eight, and Bree, nine, to come down, and snatched baby Bryce out of her playpen.

Then the unmistakable roar approached the house.

The problem the Erie weather office was facing, along with the other stations strung to the south and west of it, was lead time. Without the usual pattern of storms moving across central and western Ohio, there was little time to absorb and plot the data. It was almost inconceivable that the mammoth storms could break so suddenly overhead. It seemed as if they had dive-bombed down along the Pennsylvania-Ohio border. The supercells had started off as individual giants. Then they grew into giant clusters. Then they formed a squall line almost a hundred miles long.

Erie was on the northern end of the line. Albion was just below it. Since the line raked at an angle as it moved east, Albion was the likely target for the first major blow. But what about the other towns to the south of it, both in Ohio and Pennsylvania? Pymatuning State Park, Jamestown, Atlantic, Wheatland, and Beaver Falls were just a few of the towns that sat like ducks and could be mowed down. In Ohio, Newton Falls and Niles, just above Youngstown, were in the same position, among others.

Dave Bell kept himself glued to the radar. He scanned the cells horizontally first. Then he raised or lowered the antenna and scanned the vertical. The screen picked up the water content, but most important was to find any hook buried in the boiling cell. Usually they showed up in the southwest quadrant, and that is what he was focusing on. If he picked up a hook, he would return to the scanning procedure to plot the movement so the public could be warned downstream. It was not a foolproof operation. There was no guarantee a hook could be found; sometimes they were masked.

Every meteorologist was forced to admit that forecasting was not an exact science; often it was an art. The problem was, without the advanced Doppler radar, if you picked up a hook right over a town, the tornado probably was already on the ground and the town already had been hit hard. And even a Doppler image could provide only about twenty minutes' worth of warning.

Dave Bell, Bob Sammler, and the rest of their colleagues often sat back and tried to think of ways they could warn the public better. There was no way they could run down the street and ring an alarm bell. There was no magic formula at all. Yet the knowledge that human lives were at stake made them acutely aware of their responsibilities. They had the frustrating feeling that the warning system was not enough. Only a fraction of the public had the necessary wavelength to receive the NOAA radio warnings. Not everybody by any means had their radios or television sets turned on. One estimate was that only twenty thousand of a quarter-million sets in the area were turned on in the late afternoon. The pickup by the commercial stations often was sluggish. They could only do their damnedest.

When John Halfast arrived at 4:00 P.M. to relieve Bob Sammler, there was no sign yet that a killer tornado was heading directly toward his hometown of Albion. When he and Bob Sammler checked the alphanumeric screen at that time there was the rather hefty storm cell covering nearly two thirds of Ashtabula County, to the west of the border. It was not quite a supercell yet. But both agreed that they would go for the severe-thunderstorm warning. It went out at just about the time Kansas City flashed the tornado watch at 4:25 P.M.

Then came the first hook and Bomboy's spotter report—the killer was heading straight toward Albion. John Halfast, standing at the computer terminals, thought immediately about his wife and family. He would not leave his post under any circumstances. But he quickly picked up the phone and called his home. The line was dead. The ham radio bands suddenly were flooded with frantic messages. Most of Albion, it appeared, was wiped out.

Suddenly two more deadly hook echoes sprang on the radar screen. One was near the forests and campgrounds of Pymatuning State Park, about twelve miles southwest of Albion. The other was spotted near Jamestown and Atlantic, about the same distance below that. It appeared certain that not one but three killer tornadoes were about to ravage the northwestern corner of the state.

In Jamestown, Harold McCrea, up on an aluminum ladder and polishing his camper, suddenly noticed that the ladder was shaking. He decided to call it quits. Across the road, he saw a strange thing: Two horses suddenly had gone into a gallop and smashed themselves into the side of a barn.

Nearby in the same town, the Kineston family was relaxing. Jim Kineston, with the Pennsylvania Department of Transportation, was playing cards with his ten-year-old daughter, Susie. His wife was reading the paper in the living room. Their radio scanner was on, as it frequently was, monitoring the fire, police, and emergency channels.

When a matter-of-fact message came across that a tornado watch was in effect, Mrs. Kineston was not alarmed. Only a year or so before, she had driven to town when a tornado watch had been announced, and nothing whatever had happened. In fact, most of the people in town were rather blasé about watches or warnings, because they seldom seemed to materialize.

But ten-year-old Susie heard the message from the other room. She had been through several tornado drills at school, sponsored by the U.S. Weather Service outreach program. The moment the watch was announced, she jumped up from the card table and insisted her parents go down to the cellar. They tried to calm her down, but she gathered some blankets and a flashlight and pleaded with them to come down to the cellar with her.

Suddenly a voice came in from a ranger in Pymatuning State Park. His voice was panicky. "Tornado approaching across the lake at the campgrounds: Take cover! Take cover! Take cover!"

The camp was ten miles to the north. Outside the Kineston home, the skies blackened. Maybe she's right, Mrs. Kineston was thinking. Recalling the old wives' tale about opening the windows to release the air pressure, she went upstairs to do so while Susie began crying and pleading with them to come down to the cellar right away. Jim Kineston picked up the phone to warn a neighbor, with Susie still pleading.

Then her mother looked out the kitchen window. She saw it coming, a brownish, dirty, swirling cloud, spinning with fury. She yelled at her husband to get off the phone, and she scrambled to the cellar with Susie. Her husband followed in seconds, and they huddled in the corner by the washing machine.

Gene Hart, the assistant superintendent at the state park, had just arrived at his residence on the grounds. He was getting out his camera to take pictures of the golf-ball-size hail that suddenly began battering the countryside. Halfway out the door, the only thing he caught on his scanner was: "Take cover!"

He called back to headquarters to warn the staff; the phone

went dead. He jumped in his truck to rush there when he saw a giant, dark twister in the sky. It was moving toward Jamestown, a few miles away. Just at that moment, he heard the Jamestown fire sirens go off. They rose to high pitch, then lowered to start up the scale again. Halfway up, they suddenly died. Obviously the power had been lost. Over the car radio, the Linesville camp hostess was calling. She was worried about an elderly couple out in a boat. Then she yelled that another funnel was approaching directly toward her flimsy trailer. All trailers are helpless tin cans in a tornado. The approaching twister was a full city block wide. As she spoke, the radio was abruptly cut off.

7. /ATLANTIC IS GONE

While Skywarn spotter Richard Bomboy fielded scores of messages from the areas surrounding Albion, Fire Chief Herk Shearer approached the town center in his truck. When he reached East Pearl Street on his way to the firehouse, he was stunned. The street simply seemed to have disappeared. Trees and telephone poles were scrambled across every street and intersection he could see. House after house was literally flattened.

He spun the wheel of his truck and turned down another block. People were running from the ruins of their houses, screaming and bleeding. Cries of help came from beneath the ruins. There was no way to reach the firehouse; every main street was blocked by tons of debris. He got on his CB radio and called the firehouse, requesting every ambulance in the county to come to the town center. Every fireman was ordered to search and rescue. He finally got to the firehouse as the entire department moved out to the streets to seek the trapped, the injured, and the dead.

It was impossible to estimate the damage immediately. Over a hundred homes seemed to be wiped flat, ripped off their foundations, or stripped of their roofs and walls. As volunteers with axes and chain saws cleared the path, the fire trucks moved out, stopping by each demolished home for a house-by-house search, tracking down hidden places where moans and cries for help came from.

Meantime, State Trooper Bradley Mills dashed from his home outside Albion, commandeered the CB radio of the first car he encountered, and called the state police barracks near Erie. They dispatched every available trooper to the scene. He made his way to the temporary emergency center at the firehall, where he assisted the first-aid volunteers who were waiting for the ambulances to come with doctors, nurses, and paramedics.

As he approached the firehall, he simply could not believe what he saw. He could not recognize the streets he had walked on for the fifteen years he had lived in the town. The people he saw were dazed. They were not panicked. Some of them just said "Hi," as if nothing had happened. They looked as if they saw him but didn't see him at the same time.

His eventual assignment from headquarters: identification of the dead. He was well equipped for this. It was a gruesome job. But it had to be done. The senior high school was designated as the morgue; the junior high had previously been designated as the Red Cross disaster relief center. He headed for the high school as cars, trucks, and ambulances began to arrive with the bodies of the dead. He was used to this kind of work on the dreadful carnage of the highways. But this was different. Family and friends were frantically clustering to find out which loved ones were dead, which were missing, which were injured. It became the toughest job he had ever faced—especially when he found among the dead several of his own friends.

Local Red Cross Chairman Martha Sherman knew immediately the seriousness of the situation when she heard the county dispatcher's voice come over the scanner in her living room. But she did not yet know the magnitude of the tragedy. Making sure that her mother was placed in a chair near an inside wall, she rushed to the barn to warn her husband, Jim, that the power was out, that a tornado warning had been issued. As she approached the barn, she felt that she was almost lifted off her feet. Shrapnel was whirling in the air around her. She doubted if she could reach the barn. She did, however, and there was no sign of the funnel near her. Still, that nauseating yellow cast hung over the sky. The house and barn were unscathed. Not knowing the extent of the damage in town, she immediately got ready to drive to the junior high school in case the Red Cross emergency service was needed.

But she wondered now about her daughter-in-law, Debbie Sherman. It would be just about the time that she would be driving from work to her home on Knapp Road. In fact, Debbie was doing just that, although Martha Sherman had no way of knowing it. Debbie saw the funnel coming toward her as she entered her driveway. Her dog romped up to greet her. She picked up the dog, threw him in the car, and revved up the motor to escape the onrushing funnel. She wasn't aware that she would be driving directly toward it.

But a nearby neighbor, racing to get his tractor into the barn, saw that she was on a collision course with the giant twister. He gunned the tractor and tried to run her off the road. He was too late. Down the road, he saw the funnel literally suck the car two hundred feet up in the air. It soared over the top of the silo and crashed in a field. Debbie Sherman was dead.

Martha Sherman, organizing the Red Cross relief operation at the junior high school, worked through the night, unaware that Debbie's body was lying in the morgue in the dark, lantern-lit halls of the senior high school next door.

Bob McClymond, still in the family room of his home, put down his Manhattan and jumped to his feet when he heard the roar. It was simply a God-awful sound that defied description, a thousand jet engines, perhaps. He yelled for Ann to come downstairs, rushed her toward the cellar door in the kitchen. As he did, he saw a row of plants on the kitchen windowsill literally sucked out the window. A huge branch flew by. Then there was a sudden, deathly stillness. He looked across the street. It appeared as if Jackson Avenue was gone. The houses were flat. There was nothing but rubble. He looked up at the sky again. It was clear, calm, and blue. The savage winds were gone in a matter of seconds. Several people were trapped in their basements, yelling for help. Several firemen were already on the scene, and he ran out to help them.

Nearby was a trailer. It had all but disappeared. In it had been Kathy Kelly and her five-month-old baby, Paul, along with her mother. Kathy was feeding the infant when the winds struck. All three were blown out. Baby Paul was sucked from his mother's arms. Frantic and injured, she cried out for her baby. He was nowhere to be found. Rescuer Danny Carr raked through the rubble as mother and grandmother were rushed to St. Vincent's Hospital. Carr searched everywhere for the baby. He finally came to the railroad tracks, where he heard a faint cry. Quickly he pulled the rubble gently away as medical help arrived. The child was taken to Hamot Medical Center, and only hours later was the desperate mother reunited with him.

The haddock, french fries, and vegetables were already on the table when Linda Quay lit the last candle for the delighted children at the table. She was not too concerned about the fire call her husband had responded to; it was a frequent happening. But then she heard the overpowering roar. She saw the trees bending outside the window. Her first instinct was to go upstairs and close the windows. Then she thought better of it. Now the noise was louder, and she knew it must be a tornado. She screamed to the kids to rush to the basement, then quickly turned to blow out the candles for safety. At that moment, all the downstairs windows suddenly shattered. Shards of glass ripped through the room. She noticed a slight movement out of the corner of her eye. Then she realized in horror that the older kids had forgotten to take Bonnie Sue from her high chair. As the glass fragments sprayed across the room, Linda dropped on her knees and crawled across the dining-room floor toward the high chair. Her face and scalp and body were punctured with flying glass. With the shards still flying and timbers cracking, she continued to crawl beneath the level of the windowsill toward Bonnie Sue.

Reaching there, she grabbed the side of the chair and tipped it over to the floor, out of the range of the flying glass. Then she pulled the child out of the chair and under her chest. Painfully, with her hands and knees riddled with the broken glass that covered the floor, she reached the kitchen.

She was shocked to find the other children crying there by the cellar door. The suction was so great they could not open it. Still shielding Bonnie Sue, she tugged with all her strength until the door opened. She and the four children slid down the steps to the cellar.

In the cellar, they kept crying, "Mommy, what is it? What is it?" She tried to explain, but now the stillness outside the house was ominous. There was nothing but dead silence after that terrible roar. She was afraid to go out, afraid of what she might see when she did. It seemed as if ten minutes went by, when she heard voices and people moving around on creaking boards and planks. "Anybody here? Everybody all right?" they kept repeating.

At last she got the courage to lead the kids up the cellar stairs. The floors were a carpet of broken glass. Trees had crashed on all sides of the house, mercifully missing it. Outside, there was another carpet: a carpet of planks where the rest of the houses on the block once stood. She called out to the rescuers that everyone was all right—to go on to find others who might not be. Her thoughts were of little Andrea's mother, Anna Sobol. She had left the child in Linda's care. Was she trapped in a car in the terrible storm? And her husband, Charley? What had happened to him after he was called to the fire station?

Her one thought was: If I'm alive and safe, go and help other people. She met the Sobols walking along the railroad tracks. They were safe, thank God. They brought news of the husband, Charley. He was safe, too, joining the volunteer workers searching for the trapped, the dead, and the injured.

Meantime, downtown among those stores that had escaped undamaged, the doors were open. Without exception, the victims were told: "Take anything you want or need."

Linda Quay took her children to the disaster center at the junior high school and pitched in to help wherever she could.

*   *   *

Right after the unmistakable roar approached her house on East Pearl Street, Sandra Stahlsmith shepherded all her children into the fruit cellar. Four months pregnant and her heart pounding, she began to pray. The noise was overpowering now as she gathered them against the only wall in the cellar without a window and behind a stout table stacked high with canning jars. With six-year-old Luke under her right arm and three-year-old Zachary under her left, they pasted themselves against the wall, standing with the table in front of them. It was black and dank in the cellar. The children were crying and the baby whimpering.

Then the heart of the tornado exploded like a bombshell. There was a screaming noise and a whistle, then an enormous crashing rumble. The timbers and walls of the entire house exploded into the basement, filling it with debris. Sandra felt the wall crushing against her back. With her arm still around Luke to protect him, she felt herself pressed toward the table. She pushed back as hard as she could to stop the wall. It was impossible. She was now bent almost double. Suddenly the wall gave way more. She and Luke were crushed against the edge of the table. Luke's neck was trapped. Sandra's weight was now forced down on his head, which her unmovable chin rested on. She could smell his hair, the warm, loving scent of a child. Then she felt him take two sharp breaths and was still. The others were clear of the collapsing wall, and safe. But little Luke was no longer breathing. Sandra knew he was dead. She prayed again, thanking God that he at least did not die in agony.

The small children began crying. Still trapped, her face crushed against the canning jars, she tried to comfort them. But frozen in her agonizing position and almost suffocating, she had no hope left. There were no signs of rescuers outside, just deathly stillness. "Kids," she said, "I think we're all going to be with Jesus real soon. So let's go to sleep, and when we wake up, we'll find Him beside us."

But eight-year-old Brook spotted a gap above them in the collapsed floor. It was nearly six feet up, but she scrambled up some debris to reach it. There was still nothing but silence above.

Ten minutes went by. Then Sandra, still hopelessly trapped against the table, told her nine-year-old, "Bree, you're going to have to try to get out and find Brook and get help."

Just then, a fireman appeared at the opening. He was able to pull Bree through the hole, as well as little Zachary, who was shaking like a leaf. He tried to pull the planks from on top of Sandra and press the wall back. It was impossible. Little Luke's body still was trapped in her arm against the table. She continued to smell his hair. She felt as if her left arm was severed. There was no feeling in it.

There was barely room for the rescuer to squeeze in. He seemed to be killing himself to try to move the wall and the timbers. Finally he had to give up. He was crying as he left, begging Sandra to hang on. Fully half an hour went by. Then more firemen arrived. They jacked up the floor and the wall, but Sandra and Luke still were trapped against the table. Finally, a fireman was forced to take a sledgehammer and smash the table. It crumbled as Sandra and little Luke fell to the ground. Outside, she took off her mud-covered glasses and saw the havoc for the first time. All the houses around her were gone.

The rescue squad worked for five minutes on Luke. The attempt was fruitless. Sandra sat by his body. She refused to go to the hospital. She became hysterical, walked across the garden in shock. The hard-boiled eggs from dinner were scattered across the ground. Then she saw Luke's little bike. It was unscathed, not even bent or dented. She collapsed on top of it and burst into tears.

On the satellite pictures, the frontal assault of the giant supercells could be clearly seen, boiling puffs of white lumps that were continuing to rake eastward in a military line on an oblique angle from northeast to southwest. In Pennsylvania, Albion was hit first, at 5:05 P.M. The Pymatuning twister, just to the south of it, lagged only minutes behind as it headed toward the popular state tourist campsite at Linesville, ironically called "End of the Road." It was an idyllic retreat, with a sandy beach framing the shore, rimmed by stately pines and hardwoods. The campsite hostess had already assigned the sites for the trailers and campers for about thirty weekend vacationers who had arrived early for the weekend. Each site offered a sturdy rustic picnic table; each nestled in a shady, snug glen.

Most of the vacationers were outside their trailers, ready to relax for a two-day respite. At 5:10 P.M., barely five minutes after the savage twister had cut its path through Albion, the campers looked out across the lake toward the Ohio border. Coming toward them was a white tubular snout, writhing like a garden hose whipped by uncontrollable water pressure. As it spun toward them, it was sucking up the water and growing fatter with each foot it advanced. The campers scrambled for any cover they could find.

At this point the camp hostess grabbed her radiophone to alert Gene Hart back at the park headquarters. She was standing outside, next to her trailer. As the tornado struck the shore, she began to scream her frantic message. The trees snapped off at midtrunk or crashed to the ground, with enormous clods of roots and dirt at their bases. The trailers were hopelessly spun, crushed, and lifted, crashing back to the ground in twisted rubble. Before the hostess could finish her message, the heart of the spiraling hose came directly toward her. Her trailer lifted and capsized like a tin boat in a storm. It smashed down on top of her. She was pinned underneath it. She died instantly.

The path of destruction was two hundred feet wide. It passed through the campground in seconds. It moved on toward the village of Linesville. It left a trail of dead wildlife, including flocks of Canada geese with their eyes sucked out. At the Pennbank branch in Linesville, someone yelled in for everyone to take cover. The employees dove into the bank vault. They were unhurt; the twister stopped just short of the town, but not before it smashed and twisted homes, trees, and barns in a short but bloody three-mile northeasterly path. Underneath the barn of Gary Graham on Route 6, a horse was buried alive. Twenty-seven trailers at the campgrounds were turned into crumpled soft-drink cans. Two died; scores were injured. Later, the force of the tornado was measured. It was classed as F-2—near to the lowest and weakest on the Fujita scale. Albion's twister was classed as next to the highest: F-4 on the scale of both damage and terror, with winds nearly three times that of the fiercest hurricane.

At 5:20 P.M., barely ten minutes after the Linesville catastrophe and just after ranger Gene Hart had spotted the second tornado in his area, Harold McCrea in Jamestown was putting his aluminum ladder behind his shed when he saw the twister in the valley half a mile away. His house commanded a sweeping view of the hills and countryside surrounding him. The funnel was fat and huge and dirty, at least a quarter mile in diameter. Everywhere, birds were being blown out of the trees, far from its path.

He wanted to run for the cellar, but he stood transfixed. It seemed to be moving down the valley near Route 322 toward the east, carrying a thick spray of debris with it. Now, in the distance, it seemed to be hitting Fry Road and heading straight for the village of Atlantic, just a few miles away.

As an honorary member of the Jamestown Fire Department, he kept a scanner on his screen porch. He ran to it and snapped it on. A shaky voice was saying that all roads were impassable up to Snake and East Lake roads. There were frantic calls for ambulances and rescue workers. He felt sick at heart, for he was sure that many of his friends, both in Jamestown and Atlantic, were in its path. He grabbed every chain saw in his shop and drove off toward the town.

At the Kineston home in Jamestown, daughter Susie was having a hard time keeping her mother and father in the cellar. Her mother had left her purse in the living room and wanted to retrieve it. Then she looked out the small window above the washing machine. The trees were bent down until the tops touched the ground. She felt the house shake and an unbearable suction in the air. The picnic table lifted and smashed down, with its legs broken off. Birds were being helplessly ripped out of the trees. Jim Kineston saw two funnels rip by. Then there was utter stillness. Mrs. Kineston hugged little Susie. Without her insistence, they may not have still been alive.

Meanwhile, the giant, fat twister moved eastward, toward Atlantic, gorged with spinning debris and shrapnel. Now it had climbed the scale from an F-2 force to F-4, equal to the force of the tornado that had blitzed Albion only minutes before. At the computer terminals at the Erie weather station, Dave Bell, John Halfast, and Bob Sammler watched helplessly as the three radar hook echoes moved through Albion, Pymatuning, and Jamestown. Halfast could only wonder what had happened to his house and family in Albion; the phone lines were still down. Unlike during ordinary tornadoes, the lines were staying on the ground without lifting even temporarily. Lee Robinson at the ham radio desk continued to send out warnings downstream. Except for the relatively light Pymatuning F-2 twister, deadly enough in itself, the paths seemed destined to stay on the ground endlessly. The "ground truth" reports were coming in one after the other.

The storms were so powerful all along the line that Bell found he could pick up some very suspicious cells as far south as the Pittsburgh area, usually beyond Erie's range. He called Heckler at Pittsburgh to discover that they were spotting the same cells; both stations had a bead on them at the same time. The cells had to be megastorms. It was rare that both stations could lock into the same system. Yet the Pittsburgh region itself did not yet seem in danger.

In the confusing array of reports, no one knew exactly the extent of the damages or casualties. Rescuers were so busy searching for trapped victims and treating the injured that they had little time to organize reports that summarized the holocaust. People in Albion knew little if anything about Pymatuning and Linesville. People there knew little or nothing about Jamestown—or what was in store for Atlantic with the approaching tornado and its utterly devastating F-4 force. People living between and even close by paths of the three major clawing tornado twisters crossing over the Ohio border knew little if anything about the unprecedented fury and were totally unscathed.

Even in a street where rows of houses were literally wiped out, neighboring houses could be totally untouched.

In Ohio, the Cleveland weather station faced a bewildering blizzard of ham radio, Skywarn spotter, highway patrol, sheriff office, and citizen reports that jammed the phone lines and radio channels. From five o'clock on, Marvin Miller, Jack May, and Jerry Murphy pumped out watches and warnings in a constant stream: radar sighting of storm in Geauga County moving east at thirty-five miles an hour, large hail, and damaging winds. Special marine warning, Fairport Harbor to Ripley, New York, based on radar. Hail and gusty winds all through Lake and Ashtabula counties. Tornado touchdown on the Parkman–Mesopotamia Road, crossing Routes 87 and 45, lifting off ground at Route 322. Twenty minor injuries; fifty homes damaged or destroyed.

Critical was a tornado warning for Ashtabula County at 5:21 P.M. NOAA weather radio got it, as well as the Emergency Broadcasting System and the county sheriff's office. But a temporary AFOS crash as the data product moved from the TRS-80 equipment to AFOS delayed the warning from going out over NOAA weather wire. Cleveland, along with all the other weather stations in the path of the supercells, some of them towering up to an awesome height of sixty-three thousand feet, was in a desperate race with time.

8./ THE BOOK OF JOB

For Amishman Ammon Miller, May 31 had been an average sort of a day. Although the sultry weather made sweat come easily, the weather gave no indication of a threatening storm, in spite of rather odd cloud formations in the afternoon. His wife, Elizabeth, and daughter of the same name were doing chores around the house. His two sons were working around the barn.

Ammon, along with the rest of the Amish community of Atlantic, would be gathering in one of the Amish homes on Sunday to hear Bishop Yoder give one of his quiet sermons that extolled the virtues of a simple life uncomplicated by the trappings of modern materialism. Ammon himself, a rugged, handsome man with a jocular wit and a salty, pragmatic outlook, found little trouble in accepting the lack of conveniences of the outside world, as did his family. Not being used to such luxuries, they never missed them. Not even the radio or the TV was missed. Like the others in his community, he loved the soil, and his horse-drawn plow brought the scent of the earth close to him. He, like the others, embraced the creed "The old is of the best, and the new is of the Devil."

Out of this creed came a sturdy self-sufficiency. Elizabeth

shaped the family clothes by hand and a treadle sewing machine in plain, dark colors. Canning the family food and shaping the lovely quilts brought joy and plenitude, for the farm, like all the others, was prosperous and tidy. There was no need for insurance; the community took care of that. Underlying everything was a firm and unbreakable code: Misfortune to one man is the misfortune of all. Mutual aid was an unstinting practice, either for fellow Amish or for the "English," their non-Amish neighbors.

At about 5:20 P.M., Ammon was working in his little shop by the barn when he heard a heavy clatter on the roof. He stepped out to be greeted by a flurry of hailstones as big as mothballs. In seconds they grew to golf-ball size, then suddenly stopped. All was still. He looked at the sky, to the west. It was heavily overcast. The wind began to pick up.

Then a dark mass appeared from a low-scudding cloud. It was whirling madly and aiming directly toward him. Swirling inside it was an unbelievable mass of debris. He knew then it was a tornado.

He didn't have time to be frightened. He gathered his family together and rushed them to the cellar. Looking out the west cellar window, he could see a distinct black line to the north and a white line to the south. The funnel drifted a little to the north and then came back east.

Then the roar. It remained constant as he saw the twister sweep through his thirty-five acres of woodland, and twisting the trees in concentric circles, snapping them off, and slamming them over. Tree limbs flew by. Some of them crashed against the house; timbers shook and were ripped off. There was a sickening crash as his own house seemed to explode above him. But the floor above the cellar was holding.

He looked up to the top of a nearby hill where the three-hundred-foot-tall AT&T relay tower stood. Suddenly it bent like a reed and crashed to the ground. It took half a house away as it fell. He looked across to where his neighbors lived in a trailer. It simply was not there; it had disappeared in seconds. Making sure his own family was safe, he rushed out of the cellar to find his neighbors walking around in circles. Miraculously, they were unhurt. Their furniture was scattered on the ground. Ammon rushed to get some tarpaulins to cover the furniture to protect it from the rain. Then he went back to his own house. It was crushed beyond repair.

Amish Bishop Yoder, whose creed is that God "lets the sun come up on the good and the bad and lets it rain on the just and the unjust," had finished up his carpentry work in the village of Hartstown, just a few miles from Atlantic, and was heading home in his frail black carriage at the time when Ammon Miller was surveying the ruins of his farmhouse. There was hail falling all around him, but he knew nothing of the disaster that had already stricken Atlantic and environs. So strange was this phenomenon that many found it hard to believe: the incredible havoc taking place so near, yet people in the vicinity knowing nothing about it until they came within sight of the obliteration.

But the funnels moved swiftly. They would linger only occasionally. Towns could be wiped out in a matter of seconds, especially when hit with an F-4 force twisting at 260 miles an hour and moving across the ground at the speed of a truck roaring down a turnpike. Any car or tractor-trailer or train is lifted and thrown for three hundred feet or more. At times the twisters would suddenly change course, split into multiple vortices, rejoin, widen, narrow, or stop and grind down on a single location in relentless fury. The tongue of the Atlantic twister was wide— a quarter-mile wide—as it thundered down on the village. And as Bishop Yoder was guiding his carriage home, his wife and daughter saw it stop and stand still over Atlantic, push down and drill into the ground and houses.

After the lethal pause, they saw it swirling toward them, then suddenly change course. They saw it move to the house of a relative, Henry Ditwiler, as it spewed out heavy debris as if it were sawdust. At the Ditwiler house, Henry looked up to the sky to see an unbelievable sight: There were complete mobile homes spinning around inside the funnel. He yelled for his family to dive for the cellar. They did. But elderly Andy Byler was slow. He was killed as he was whipped through the air and thrown into a gulley several hundred feet away. Meantime, Henry Ditwiler's house was picked up in the air and thrown against his neighbor's house. In the cellar, he and the rest of his family survived. At Rocky Glen Cemetery, overlooking the town, tombstones were toppled, grave markers ripped and thrown from their graves. An unknown voice came over a CB radio: "Atlantic is gone."

Without a radio, Bishop Yoder did not hear that message. But when he pulled his carriage up to his damaged home, the scene that greeted him was devastating. He thanked God his immediate family was safe. Then he thought of what had to be done. The spiritual strength of the Amish is equaled only by their capacity to rally in time of need. He recalled a recent time when the barn of one of his neighbors was struck by lightning and burned to the ground. Within two days, two hundred Amishmen showed up at the site at eight in the morning. By eleven o'clock, a spanking new barn was totally completed down to the last nail.

How could this be done in such an organized way? Bishop Yoder commented one time: "There's enough carpenters around so that if somebody does something wrong, they soon tell 'em." And his further comment in times of need was equally succinct: "In fire or storm, we just get together and do it." Viewing the ruins of his town, his mind was on two things: a fitting memorial service for Andy Byler, and an immediate start on raising Atlantic, phoenixlike, from its ashes.

Reverend Charles Polley of the Atlantic Congregational Church was just leaving Meadville at about 5:00 P.M. when the golf-ball-size hail clattered against his car. But quite as suddenly, the sun came out again. He stopped for a bite at a roadside restaurant on Route 322 called the Strudel Factory. Another customer came in and quietly told him: "A town down the road has just been wiped out by a tornado."

Polley jumped into his car and headed toward Atlantic. Nearing there, he found himself dodging around fallen trees and telephone poles. Closer, he saw and heard the flashing lights and sirens of a caravan of police cars and ambulances. At the town center, not a single house remained. The post office was gone.

Nearly every tree was sheared off at stump level. The few left standing bore black, shattered limbs reaching grotesquely to the sky. The scene looked worse than any war zone pictures he had ever seen. Several bodies were being loaded into ambulances. All those killed were from a trailer park at the edge of Atlantic. A few mobile homes were squashed like accordions. Most had simply vanished. Five people died there, three in a house adjoining the trailer park. Meanwhile, the tornado moved on, fifty miles to the east, crushing everything that stood in its path. The population was more sparse, the communities few, but the results were still tragic.

By some miracle, the church in Atlantic was still standing—the only building in the center of town. Around it, beside house after house that were crushed and flat as pancakes, people seemed to be walking in circles, in shock. The reverend thanked the Lord that many people had been away for their late Friday shopping.

When Reverend Polley entered the church, there was a gaping hole in the roof above the altar. The chalice was bent at a rakish angle. The American flag and its staff were gone; the Christian flag still was there. The hymn numbers were blown out of the board. The large Bible was still on the pulpit. It was open to the Book of Job. On the right-hand page, Job 1:19 caught his eye: "Your sons and daughters were eating and drinking in the eldest brother's house when suddenly a whirlwind swept across the desert and struck the four corners of the house and it fell on the young people and killed them. . . ."

Within the hour Polley and an army of rescue volunteers set up a relief center, where the Amish and the "English" worked side by side. Months later, they would still be working there.

The National Weather Service stations in Cleveland, Erie, Youngstown, and Pittsburgh were continuing desperately to keep up with the flood of reports from spotters and amateur radio operators and their own rushing stream of weather data, which were changing from minute to minute. Without receiving the report of a tornado on the ground, or without a clearly discerned hook echo, a warning had to be issued with the greatest of caution to avoid a series of false alarms. Under these circumstances, Erie had been unable to flash a tornado warning until 5:13 P.M., only two minutes ahead of the Albion tornado and three minutes after the one at Pymatuning.

NOAA weather radio was continuing to pour out information steadily, but ordinary radio sets do not carry that band. Although a radio that is so equipped can be purchased at a fairly cheap price, few of the public have done so. The Emergency Broadcasting System was continuing to flash out the watches and warnings, but only a fraction of the public caught them. The TV crawls carrying the alerts had to fight against public indifference—and the fact that most stations carrying CNN, ESPN, and Home Box Office were not equipped to cut into programs for the cause of public safety. The only real impact on a town could come from the fire sirens—but if the electricity is cut, they become worthless. The towering storms were battling successfully against almost any device that man could shape, especially if it depended on electricity. Power lines had no armor against practically unmeasurable winds.

With the enormous storm system, lumpish and titanic, sweeping eastward on a hundred-or-more-mile front, the question was: Were more tornadoes in store? The fact that two with the force of F-4 had blasted Albion and Atlantic was unheard of in this part of the country. The expected damage at each point of the Fujita scale was clearly defined—and ominous. Since no instruments could measure the wind directly, the scale intensity was determined only after the storm had passed and the posttornado damage studied in detail.

Most feared was the F-5 tornado. With its 360-mile-an-hour winds, it was grudgingly credited with being able to destroy almost anything except the core of nuclear reactors—and they have never been tested under such incomprehensible conditions.

No F-5 tornadoes had ever occurred in this region of Ohio or Pennsylvania. The results in such a heavily populated area would be almost unthinkable. With the surprising force of the Albion and Atlantic twisters at the F-4 level now spent at those locations, the hope was that at least the rest of the region would be spared from the ravages of such violence. Still, the line of supercells was trailing eastward on the diagonal, so that even though the worst of the northern section had passed, the middle and southern sections of the squall line still had not released their fury in either violent storms or tornadoes.

But the potential was there, and the weather stations did not let down their guard. Most important was the interaction among the weather stations. They depended on each other with the fragmented "ground truth" information and the jammed radio channels.

At 5:40 P.M., Marvin Miller in Cleveland got on the phone to coordinate with the National Weather Service office at the Youngstown airport. So did Chuck Heckler in Pittsburgh. Both desperately needed Youngstown to fill the gap between their stations. But the line was dead. Lightning and winds had completely shut down the Youngstown station. Its computers and phones and instruments were dead. And the outage came just at the time when the most powerful tornadoes in history were sweeping directly toward the Youngstown area with the greatest force on the scale: F-5.

9./NO BINGO TODAY

The three communities of Newton Falls and Niles, in Ohio, and Wheatland, just over the Pennsylvania border, are suburbs that almost touch the borders of Youngstown. In Ohio, the flat billiard-table plains provide straight-line roads in checkerboard fashion, uninterrupted by the sort of hills that rise at Wheatland, where the foothills of the Alleghenies begin.

In Newton Falls, Clayton Reakes was at work at the Trumbull Pattern Works. It was a small, prosperous company and he took a great deal of pride in it. A graying, congenial gentleman with a ready smile, he continued during the day to keep an ear out for reports of heavy weather coming over the NOAA weather radio. By four-thirty that afternoon, well over an hour before Albion and Atlantic had been all but obliterated, he was not too disturbed by the impending severe-weather forecasts, since tornadoes had not yet been mentioned as a possibility. In spite of his conscientious devotion to the Newton Falls Public Safety Reserve, he was not an alarmist.

But at four twenty-five, when the tornado watch issued by Steve Weiss in Kansas City came over the air, he lost no time going into action. As usual, he expected to be ribbed for his precaution. His good-natured critics never stopped reminding him about the string of false tornado alarms he had responded to over the years. He would always shrug them off with equal good nature.

When the National Severe Storms Forecast Center pronounced that conditions were favorable for a tornado forming somewhere in the area, he respected their expertise in spite of the fact that they could never pinpoint exactly where the twister in the supercell might be lurking and ready to spring. A "watch" region of ten to twenty-five thousand square miles' worth of supercells was as confounding as a needle in a haystack, even more so. But in the light of the potential unleashed power, Reakes considered climbing the iron rungs to the roof of the Municipal Building a minor inconvenience. And May 31 was the prime time of the tornado season; anything could happen.

He arrived at the rooftop shortly after the tornado watch had been issued. As a member of the National Weather Service's Skywarn network, he was aware that it was principally through himself and the other spotters that an actual tornado warning would be issued. He also knew more than any layman that only a matter of seconds could mean the difference between life and death.

On the roof, the flat country to the west stretched out in front of him in a wide vista. The sky was a peculiar gray color, and he found that sunglasses rather than binoculars sharpened his vision better. He tuned his NOAA weather radio to 162.400 megahertz and kept his walkie-talkie ready at hand. The front was approaching, and while it looked ominous, there was nothing special to note as far as actual danger was concerned. The towering thunderheads were there, but they were in the distance. He kept his eye out for the ugly mammatus clouds with their bulging pouches, and for wind-torn, twisting, and rolling clouds that spelled trouble ahead. Then, of course, the actual funnel cloud or a pendant at the base of a cumulonimbus. Reakes would be ready for this. He would radio the dispatcher downstairs in the Municipal Hall to hit the fire siren, and to call the National Weather Service immediately, either by phone or by radio if the lines were down.

This was the procedure. But it had been set up many times

before without any threat finally developing. Reakes continued his watch as five o'clock approached. There was still no sign of a tornado to report.

Larry Sembach, Reakes's lieutenant in the Public Safety Reserves, finished up work at the phone company in nearby Hudson, Ohio, and began driving toward his Newton Falls home at about five. Turning on his AM radio in his pickup truck, he heard the tornado watch come over and immediately turned off the radio and flicked his scanner on. Still driving, he heard an alert tone come on the scanner at five-ten. His first thought was that this was merely a test, for the weather seemed fair enough.

But soon two more alerts came over the channel: possible tornado touch-downs to two nearby Ohio towns to the west. There was no indication of their severity, but he increased his speed to get in range of the Newton Falls police radio. The dispatcher told him that Reakes was already on the roof. By five-thirty, Sembach reached the Municipal Hall. He immediately called his wife and told her to keep the kids close by, in the yard. Then he joined Reakes on the roof.

They watched patiently for almost an hour. The sky began growing darker, and the wind increased. As it grew stronger, they had a hard time keeping their footing. Down below in the courtyard parking lot by the American Legion hall, the ladies were beginning to arrive for the regular weekly bingo game. They leaned against the wind and entered the hall, waving to Reakes and Sembach as they did so. Reakes answered their greeting with a stern warning: "There's a bad storm brewing; if you hear the siren go off, get under the tables or into the basement. You will have very little time." They cheerfully acknowledged the warning and continued into the hall, nearly 150 of them. Among them was Betsy Atkins. She had only recently broken her leg. Her daughter was pushing her in a wheelchair. None of the ladies liked to miss this pastime, come high winds or broken legs.

Reakes was concerned about the hall. It had a large roof that covered a wide, open area. Gymnasiums and auditoriums like this had a bad track record in tornadoes. There were no interior walls to support them. Many had suspended ceilings. They most often depended on large I-beams that could be lethal when ripped or even bent by the tornadic winds. In Louisiana, a twenty-four-foot steel beam was hurled like a javelin eight feet deep into the ground. Once a two-by-four was shot through a solid iron wall.

Knowing the deadly potential, Reakes continued to warn the bingo players as they filed in, above all for them to listen for the fire siren if it went off. As he did, Larry Sembach was noticing other things. A dog on a chain down below began violently barking and straining for no apparent reason. All the birds in the area had stopped flying. Then he saw a large black cloud in the distance. If nothing else, a cloud like this meant trouble—and fallen trees. "I'd better get home and change and get my chain saw," he told Reakes. Reakes agreed. Falling trees were common in a storm like the one that was approaching, even without a tornado.

Sembach took off, and Reakes continued his watch. Then, only minutes after Sembach had left, he saw it coming. It was about three miles away, and it was enormous and fearsome. It was heading toward Newton Falls near the underpass at Holcomb Road. Then came the roar. As with nearly everyone who ever heard a tornado, it sounded like a thousand locomotives roaring toward the center of the town, down Charleston Road, toward the Municipal Building itself, where he was standing on the exposed roof.

He yelled into his walkie-talkie to police dispatcher John Swensen, down on the first floor: "Hit the sirens, and take cover!" Within seconds, the sirens went off. Reakes watched the twister, now heading toward the downtown section, just off to his left: Main Street. The tornado was gargantuan. Neither he nor anyone else yet knew that an F-5 force was in the making, the highest point of the Fujita scale, fiercer than at Albion, fiercer than at Atlantic. It was over a quarter-mile wide at the base. Like the others, it was choked with wildly spinning debris inside and outside the funnel.

It made an erratic turn at Fourth Street, then aimed again directly at where Reakes was watching, toward the Municipal Building, toward the American Legion hall. Reakes leaped toward the hatch in the roof, then closed the latch tightly after him. Next he slid down the steel ladder rungs anchored in the wall, barely touching them with his feet. The sturdy brick building began to shake. At the basement stairs he almost collided with the police staff diving for the cellar. The suction was so great they were all sucked down the stairs with it. All the inside doors were suddenly sucked through their frames. Then, for a few moments, there was a deathly silence.

Larry Sembach reached home at about six-thirty, just before John Swensen hit the siren button. The trees were bending, branches were coming off, but none had yet fallen. Hail started to come down, not round but in the shape of thick needles. Holding his hand-held radio, he pulled in the driveway. Then he heard Reakes's frantic voice on the radio calling for the fire siren. He listened as the siren started almost immediately. It rose to its highest pitch, then lowered and started up again. When it reached the maximum again, it cut off abruptly and never started down. My God, Sembach was thinking, the twister must have hit the town. It wasn't the sound of the siren dying down; it just stopped abruptly.

Sembach yelled to his wife, Carolyn, to get herself and the kids to the cellar. He almost forgot his mother-in-law in a tiny cottage next to the house. He called his husky son Matthew to lead her to the basement. But she was moving too slowly. Matthew whisked her off her feet and carried her down the cellar stairs. "Matthew," she yelled, "you're going to drop me!"

With his family in the cellar, Sembach stood on the lawn in front of his house and watched the funnel approach. It was coming toward him in a line that would have to cross over the American Legion hall and the Municipal Building. Sembach shuddered at the thought of what might have already happened there. He watched the twister split in two as it passed around the town water tower. He retreated from the lawn to the front door of his house. Down his quiet residential street, he saw shingles suddenly ripped off the roofs of several homes. For some reason, he was transfixed as he watched two houses picked up and dropped down with a thud. Then a large building suddenly soared sky-ward, high in the sky, and exploded.

The smaller of the two funnels was coming toward him, the larger roaring down the railroad tracks that paralleled his street. A slow freight train pulling a long line of coal cars began bounc-ing up and down on the tracks. Then the bodies of the cars lifted from their wheels, spun in the air, and crashed down again. The funnel coming toward him was transparent, fading in and out. At times he could see only the debris whirling: a mass of two-by-fours and roof trusses—and a whole garage tumbling in the air above him. The roar was deafening.

The wind now was so strong that Sembach could hardly breathe. He shook himself from his trancelike state and ran to the door. It had already been wrenched off its hinges. He ran across the living room and dove for the cellar headfirst and huddled with his fam-ily. He thought of only one thing to say: "Newton Falls is gone. I don't see how anything can be left standing." The roar disap-peared as quickly as it had come. It took only seconds before the silence descended.

He came up the cellar stairs cautiously. He was surprised that the house was still standing. Compared to the other houses on the street, its damage appeared slight. The small cottage of his mother-in-law was twisted and wrenched off its foundation. But the trees everywhere were in a virtually impassable tangle. Nine enormous ones were flat on the ground surrounding his house. He could see only a mass of green leaves everywhere he looked. Incredibly, the sky above was bright and blue.

He knew he was needed downtown, and he dreaded at what he would find there. He called to Carolyn to see what she could do for the neighbors, but to watch out for broken wires that were dangling everywhere from the truncated or tumbled poles. As her husband drove around trees, over lawns, and up on the sidewalk to get downtown, Carolyn rushed out to check her neighbors. One woman was already sweeping her sidewalk. She looked calm enough at first, but it was plain that she was in deep shock, working like an automaton. Another woman was raking leaves, the same blank look on her face, while around her lay the ruins of her house. Almost like zombies, they barely responded to

Carolyn's questions. Miraculously, she learned, no one on the street had been killed—including the freight train crew who had been lifted off the track.

Zigzagging his truck toward town, Larry Sembach found all the streets blocked, but he was able to continue over more front lawns and backyards to reach the Municipal Building, which was the only structure in the area still standing almost intact. The Sohio gas station across the street had simply vanished. So had the post office. The whole roof of the large pharmacy was gone. Police and firemen were already giving first aid to the moaning, the screaming, and the bleeding.

He looked over at the American Legion hall. The roof was half ripped off. The eighteen-inch steel I-beams were precariously perched within an inch of toppling into the hall. For the most part, the hall was in ruins. He could not imagine what had happened inside.

Just before the fire sirens had gone off, American Legion adjutant Don Bowers had the tables prepared and the bingo game ready to go. Bowers and the rest of the players had heard the warning that Reakes had yelled from his lookout post on the roof. But with the game ready to start, it was not preeminent in the minds of the 150 enthusiasts with their bingo boards and pieces neatly in front of them over a wide expanse of tables. The first numbers had barely been called when the sirens went off, and with it the unmistakable rumble of the tornado.

Bowers yelled loudly for everyone to hit the floor and get under the tables. There was a wild scramble. The women dove under, piling on each other in disarray. Reakes's warning had taken effect; they lost no time. Betsy Atkins's daughter unceremoniously dumped her mother's wheelchair over and slid it sideways under the table. The mother screamed as she did so. "Hell, I'd rather have you break another leg," the daughter yelled back, "than for you to get killed!" She and the others weren't a minute too soon.

For some reason, one of the ladies screamed that she had to rush to her car to save her wedding pictures. They tried to stop her, but she was out the door in seconds. The roar grew louder. Over it they heard the yells of the lady outside trying to get back in. She was hanging on to the door desperately. Someone forced it open, and she came back in. The tornado hit. The roof began to peel off. The giant steel girders slid toward the edge of the supporting walls. The smell of escaping gas filled the room. Bowers yelled for everyone to douse their cigarettes.

For nearly ten minutes the group cowered under the tables as the invisible cloud of gas hung over them. Above them, many of the bingo cards lay neatly untouched, the pieces remaining exactly in place. The cigarettes were out, but no one could be sure a spark could not ignite from the tangled wires inside or outside the building.

When Larry Sembach reached the American Legion hall, the women finally were streaming out of the building. Amazingly, there were few injuries. The minute he smelled the gas, he called on his radio to the Ohio Highway Patrol to order Ohio Edison to shut off all the mains. A fireman cautiously approached the toppled gas meters with a spanner wrench. A bystander offered to help, and the fireman handed him the wrench while he went back to get another. "Hey," the bystander called after him, "I just offered to help. I don't want to be a hero." Incredibly, one of the bingo ladies asked Bowers if they were going to honor the cards already played.

Sembach warned the bingo players to stay away from the downed wires and to clear the area as soon as possible. Then he pitched in to join with Reakes in the rescue efforts all through the town. What the toll would be, nobody knew.

Just before the sirens blew, the bride and groom who were soon to be Mr. and Mrs. Ronald Taylor prepared to walk down the glassed-in hallway that led to the chapel of the Church of God. It was a few blocks away from the Municipal Building, where Reakes had been maintaining his lookout. Apprentice minister Robert Benak would be performing the ceremony. It was a small, private affair, but the bride and groom and wedding party would be in their best finery and in the best of spirits.

As the appointed hour approached, the party solemnly lined up in the hallway in meticulous order, somewhat distracted by the hail that suddenly began lashing the wide glass windows that framed the hall. The bride adjusted her veil. The best man nervously rubbed the wedding ring he was holding in his fingers. The bride's mother wiped a small tear away from her eye.

The minister gave the signal. The organist struck up the first notes of "Here Comes the Bride." The wedding party took the first steps toward the chapel doorway. Then the hallway windows exploded. The glass shrapnel filled the air. The entire party dropped to the floor below the level of the sills, cut and bleeding. All the finery was spattered with blood. A late arrival for the wedding felt her car rise high in the air as she pulled into the parking lot. It crashed down and she jumped out, unhurt.

In the parsonage next to the church, the Reverend Lillie McCutcheon and her husband, Glenn, had just finished their evening meal. Outside the doorway were two elegant baskets of flowers, Mother's Day gifts of their two married sons. The minute Lillie McCutcheon heard the hail clattering outside, she ran to the front door to bring the flowers in. They were being whipped by the rising wind, and she quickly stepped back in the front hall and tried to close the door. The rush of the wind made it impossible. Her husband rose from the dining-room table to help.

Together they pushed with all their strength. The door would not move. They heard the monstrous sound of a thousand trains coming toward them. The heavy front door snapped backward. It pinned them both against the hallway wall with an irresistible force. A metal awning outside the dining room window was smashed into knife blades to slit the dinner table where Glenn had been sitting. All the windows in the house splintered. The roof and floor above them rose in the air and disappeared, carrying the large chandelier with it. The suction was unbearable. If they had not been so tightly pinned, they may have been swept away with the roof. Every wall in the house was smashed down and whipped away—except the lone hallway wall that they were pinned against.

As the roof disappeared, a blizzard of pink, powdery insulation smothered them. It packed their eyes and ears and mouths so they could hardly breathe. Across the street, an entire house lifted and turned off its foundation. Its roof soared through the air toward the church. Part of it crashed into the top of the church. The other skidded through the parking lot, smashing every car in it. The McCutcheon garage was yanked off its foundation and also disappeared. Two enormous trees javelined through the roof of the chapel.

Lillie McCutcheon, choked by the insulation and unable to call for help, was wedged so that her hand and wrist were jammed above the door. Her husband, equally mute, was unable to move in any direction. How long they were jammed there they did not know. But soon they heard the voices of two carpenters who had been working in the basement of the church. They were clawing through the debris, desperately trying to find the McCutcheons.

One of them was yelling, "Here's one of their cars in the driveway! Wait—here's the other. Where are they? Where are they? Why don't they answer?" Still unable to respond vocally, Lillie McCutcheon desperately waved her hand that poked over the doorway. Finally, the workers saw it. They rushed to the door and forced it open. Except for bruises and cuts, the McCutcheons were unhurt. They considered it a miracle.

So did the wedding party. The marriage was performed an hour later in tattered clothes with battered and bandaged guests. To Reverend McCutcheon, the creed of her church—God can do anything—held a new meaning.

Just down the street, the post office had literally vanished. Much of the town was a shambles. But thanks to Reakes's timely warning, no one in Newton Falls was killed. The entire town considered this a miracle.

10. THE LINES ARE DOWN

With the Cleveland and Pittsburgh weather offices covering for the crippled Youngstown station, Niles expected severe thunderstorms. But an F-5 tornado was a quantum leap beyond that. The NOAA weather reports were critically important, but their coverage was confined to a range limit of forty miles. Akron, Erie, and Pittsburgh transmitters were working full blast to keep up with the warnings that were now practically overlapping each other. Few citizens were equipped to receive them directly. They had to depend on secondhand transmissions from the broadcast media that in turn had little lead time to prepare the messages and get them out. Ironic was the fact that the F-5 tornado that had already hit Newton Falls and that was on a headlong rush toward Niles was cutting a path across an area that was out of the range of the three transmitters involved.

Ohio had a system called the Law Enforcement Automated Data System, known as LEADS, that provided automated weather warnings to the Highway Patrol, sheriffs' offices, and local police. It was maintained on a Sperry Univac 1100-83 computer, and it needed little human intervention to speed the critical reports it carried. Still there was a lag because the "ground truth" of the Skywarn spotters often would come seconds before a community was about to be blasted. Pennsylvania had a similar system, dubbed CLEAN, standing for the Commonwealth Law Enforcement Agency Network. It required a relay through Harrisburg, far to the east, where reports had to be typed up manually, with a subsequent delay, especially when messages flooded the wires.

Compounding the problem of forewarning the population of inevitable disaster was the stunned and incredulous reaction of those who happened to see a tornado approach or pass by at a near distance. The force, the power, the violence were so awesome that the observer became stunned or paralyzed. Behavior patterns became bizarre. At a pleasant roadside picnic park halfway between Newton Falls and Niles, a group of relaxed vacationers were sitting at redwood tables enjoying a picnic supper just as the F-5 tornado roared along its direct path toward Niles.

One of them had a TV camera. As the overpowering giant twister moved closer, running parallel to the parking lot of the picnic grounds, the vacationer grabbed his camera and began taping it. It was a sickening sight, especially with the debris of housetops, walls, and planks spinning in and around it. The top of the funnel must have been half a mile wide. The base of the snout hitting the ground was out of the camera range, blocked by a long ridge of hills. The midsection was thick and barrel-shaped, but in the form of a twisted rope. It was only a few hundred yards away at the most. Strangely, the sky was clear and blue all around.

The camera panned with the monstrous killer as it moved from left to right at an apparent speed of forty miles an hour. It was inexorable, unstoppable, and utterly terrifying. In the foreground of the camera frame a cluster of spectators, a dozen or so, could be seen in the foreground of the lens. One man in a T-shirt stood by his car, his hands on his hips, as calmly as if he were watching a flock of geese moving across the sky.

"Gee," he could be heard saying on the soundtrack. "Look at that."

A voice spoke up off-screen. "You know, I'll bet that's a tornado." Both voices were calm and relaxed.

"Yeah," the man in the T-shirt replied. "I guess it is."

"What do you know," said another voice.

"Looks like flying saucers inside the thing," a fourth voice spoke.

"Sure does," someone answered, and followed with a chuckle.

The entire group remained completely impassive as the tornado moved on. The man in the T-shirt sauntered calmly to his car and got in it. Four or five people walked casually back toward the picnic tables. The sun continued to shine. No one ran to find a phone or a car with a CB radio in it. No one headed for a ditch or hit the ground. And yet the biggest maxitornado in the region's history had just passed close by, and was continuing on its way to the unsuspecting town of Niles, just a few miles to the east and now only minutes away.

It could be that the people at the picnic grounds were stunned from the magnitude of the sight, or simply overwhelmed with awe. But the scene dramatized the fact that there was a razor's edge between total devastation from a twister's force—or relaxed safety just outside the path. People and structures just a few feet from either side of the base of the funnel could be magically unscathed. A few feet inside the funnel, everything could be pulverized. Fate and destiny played the biggest role even in the age of science. The freakishly capricious funnel had luckily just grazed the main town of Newton Falls, in spite of the fury that had created such havoc in many places there. Also, the vigilance of Clayton Reakes had contributed heavily to the fact that no human lives were lost.

The path of the tornado, growing in force to the maximum of the F-5 classification, made it inevitable that Niles would be hit. Just where in the town it would strike would spell the difference between life and death—and destruction.

A few months before May 31, Fire Lieutenant John Hughes was at Niles Fire Station Number 1, going over routine business with Chief Charley Semple. Hughes, a rugged and congenial fire fighter in his thirties, turned to speak to Semple, who was standing beside the desk. The quarters were rather cramped there, and in turning he noticed that the chief had accidentally knocked the large-scale map of the town from the wall. The wooden frame was damaged in the fall. Chiding Semple for his clumsiness, Hughes told his chief not to worry. He would do a new map and bring the old one up to date. In fact, parts of the town were completely missing on the old map. It needed to be extended to include newer parts of town.

"Tell you what, Chief," Hughes told Semple. "If we ever have a disaster or something like that, we'll be a lot better prepared for it."

Chief Semple agreed, and Hughes went to work on his new map. Long before May 31, it was in place and showing more detail, to include everything from the Niles Park Plaza, the shopping center up on the strip on Route 422, the Niles Roller Rink, and a spanking new five-million-dollar nursing home next to them and just ready to open its doors. It of course included Fire Station Number 2, up on the Niles–Courtland Road, halfway between the town center and the strip, next to the Union Cemetery. Inside the trim brick structure of Fire Station Number 2 were the shiny, spit-and-polish engines that were always kept in readiness, the pride of the department.

Through the afternoon, sporadic weather reports were coming over the broadcast media, but for the most part, few people in Niles paid any great attention to them. As one resident of Niles commented later, "Everybody says, 'It's just another weather watch. We get them all the time.' I don't think anyone even gave it a thought."

Fire fighter Gene Crockett, at the watch desk just off the bay floor of Station Number 2, was preoccupied with routine paperwork when he heard what he thought was a low-flying helicopter. He had been in the service and was curious about the different types of choppers, so he sauntered over to the open fire station doorway to see what kind of craft was coming over. Ron Rinaldi, another fireman on duty, joined him at the doorway. The station commanded a sweeping view of the valley to the west.

Then they saw it. It looked like a tidal wave in the distance rolling toward them, spinning like a top. It was approaching from the southwest, thick and barrel-shaped, dark gray, filled with

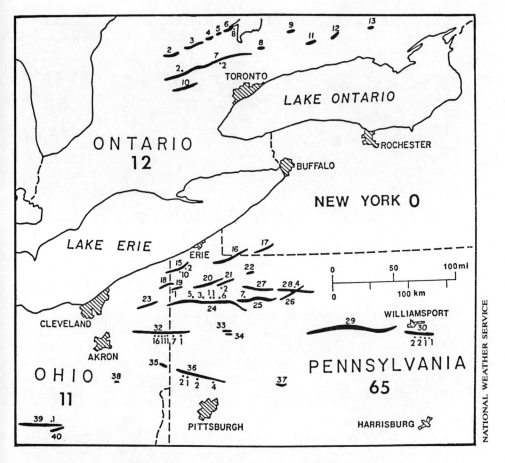

The National Weather Service map showing
the track of the killer tornadoes
in Ohio, Pennsylvania,
New York, and Canada

Ten days later a second tornado begins to bulge near Albion
in northwest Pennsylvania.

The wall cloud darkens—the
forerunner of a tornado.

The rotation within the wall cloud
becomes more concentrated.

The funnel turns into a tight spiral just
before touchdown—and just before striking the
home of the photographer!

The Area Shopper, CONNEAUTVILLE, PENNSYLVANIA

The heart of Albion lies pulverized
after the tornado passed.

Wreckage in Albion

This was once a trailer
camp near Atlantic.

When radio station WWIZ went off the air,
its tower turned into a pretzel, and many
listeners had their first inkling
of the coming disaster.

Searchers in Albion look for the
dead or missing.

Amish and Mennonite ladies joined their menfolk
in the relief effort at Atlantic, traveling
miles in their fragile, horse-drawn
black carriages.

smothering dust. It was thundering across Warren Road, grinding right over the old Republic Steel plant, through St. John and Woodglen avenues and across Mosquito Creek, just missing the Bonham School.

As it grew closer, Crockett saw several small, snakelike twisters inside the large funnel. It seemed as if there were shingles spinning around inside and outside the quarter-mile-wide diameter. But when it spun still closer, he realized that the "shingles" were much more than that: They were half roofs, huge plywood panels, sheet metal, trusses, two-by-fours. It seemed to be obliterating everything in its path.

Crockett and Rinaldi were both transfixed by the sight, almost hypnotized. "We stood there in shock, not bravery," Crockett later said. They didn't even talk to each other. The sound changed from that of a helicopter to the inevitable sound of roaring trains. Then they could discern the shocking sight of several automobiles, turning, twisting in the air, high up in the funnel. They both grabbed their fire helmets, and dove for the inside bathroom, huddled down in a corner.

Outside, the air was full of weird sounds. They could hear the trees cracking loudly, like fireworks, big trees that surrounded the station. Then the walls and roof of the fire station were peppered with shrapnel that seemed to explode against the building. The furniture, beds, chairs, a sofa were tossed around inside and then sucked out the back of the building. Broken glass was everywhere.

As the sound receded, Crockett and Rinaldi cautiously came out from hiding. The building was still intact except for the windows. The engines were unharmed. In the driveway, a car was dumped with a ten-foot two-by-four stuck completely through the front tire. It was impossible to get an engine out of the house. Not only was the car blocking the road, but also the fallen trees made the driveway impassable.

They looked to the left, to the cemetery. The tombstones were ripped out of the ground and scattered like dominoes. All the trees were down. But most shocking were the cars. Over twenty of them were strewn across the grounds, smashed almost beyond recognition. Piles of tires from Carmen's Auto Service were strewn among the wreckage. The cemetery had changed to a junkyard.

Farther to the left, the road was nowhere to be seen, blanketed with trees and the rubble of the houses and buildings that had stood there only seconds before. They were literally wiped out. The radio in the engine cab was screaming with overlapping messages. Phone lines were down. They heard the sirens go off downtown. The engines were trapped. They could go nowhere. A clear message came over the radio to Station Number 2: The Convenient Food Mart just down the road from the firehouse was smashed flat. Gas was escaping. People were trapped. It was near enough to get there by foot. Crockett and Rinaldi grabbed a spanner wrench, axes, and other tools. They climbed over trees, over a hill, and reached the store in minutes.

Only a few moments before, Marie Gregorich was working the 2:00 P.M. to 8:30 P.M. shift at the store. It was in the usual format for a convenience store: the cashier counter, long racks of canned foods and breadstuffs, refrigerated coolers for drinks and frozen foods. A few customers were browsing through the aisles for their last-minute Friday-evening shopping.

The sky had a strange overcast to it, but Marie took little notice of it. A customer just outside the front door poked her head in and said, "Hey, you'd better come out and take a look at this."

Marie did so. She looked to the west over a section of town called the Cynthia area. Several homes were exploding as the twister swept across them. She ran into the store and yelled to manager Mike Pissini that they were right in the path of a tornado. He looked out a back window and immediately yelled for Marie to get out of the way of the glass windows and duck for cover. She grabbed hold of the base of a counter and fell flat as the store was hit. The walls collapsed and toppled in the form of a tepee. The cans and foodstuffs sprayed through the air as the tall cooler cabinets toppled. Trapped in the wreckage were four women and a little girl, as well as Marie and the manager.

When Crockett arrived, the first thing he did was take the spanner wrench and shut off the gas valve. The gas stopped hissing. Inside, the little girl was screaming that they were trapped. A fire truck from Station Number 1 arrived, and together the crews tried to pry the wreckage off the entrapped victims. It was too big to remove by hand. Quickly they took a wrecker hook chain and pulled the whole wall back. They took the little girl out first. Crockett thanked God she was safe; like nearly every other fireman, he had the strength to face any kind of human calamity except when it came to kids.

At the time that the funnel was roaring through Niles, Fire Lieutenant Hughes was leisurely driving home from the nearby town of Hubbard. His wife, Christine, was at home with the three children: eighteen-year-old John and two smaller ones. About ten miles out of Niles, Hughes reached Tibbett's Wick Road to find traffic backed up for an unknown distance ahead, moving erratically. His first reaction was that there must be a major fire somewhere. In moments, ambulances and highway patrol cars squeezed through the jammed traffic. He finally called out to an ambulance driver to ask where the fire was. There was no fire, he was told, there was a tornado, and every ambulance in the county was being called in. "Better get back to your town," the ambulance driver told him. "They'll need you."

With his fire credentials, Hughes joined the police cars and ambulances to move at all possible speed to Niles. Entering town, he was puzzled. He could see no damage at all. He swung by his house. It was unscathed. On his way to phone the fire department for orders, his wife told him that young John had herded them all to the basement, as he had learned to do at school drills.

Hughes could not get through on the phone, and he drove swiftly to the downtown Fire Station Number 1. Still there was no evidence of damage. As he got his boots and helmet, Captain Tom Leonard sent him to the Convenient Food Mart. On the way there he suddenly came upon the wide swath of ruins. The devastation was unbelievable. One house on a side street sat in the middle of the road. Not a utility pole in the path of the twister was left standing. Trees were either flat on the ground, or standing with shredded black arms reaching toward the sky. Everywhere were smashed autos, looking as if they were sandblasted, with windshields and windows sucked out of them.

He was able to reach the Convenient Food Mart, where Gene Crockett and other fire fighters and police had completed the search and rescue. Orders from Chief Charley Semple were to search one area, one building at a time. Hughes helped remove the woman who was killed, and then moved on to the Niles Park Plaza on the Route 422 strip. Radio reports were flooding the channels: The entire area there was in ruins.

As Hughes approached the location, he was astounded. He kept asking himself: Where's the shopping plaza? Where's the roller rink? Where's the new nursing home? They simply seemed to have disappeared. With such devastation throughout the town, he wondered now if even the disaster map he had so carefully prepared would be of any help.

Chief Charley Semple was off duty at the moment the town was hit. Joining the region's devotion to softball, he was coaching an all-girl championship team for its upcoming battles, when two men came running to the field to yell that a tornado was coming. He sent everyone to take cover and ran to his home nearby. Sending his family to the cellar, he stood by the front door to scan the sky. He saw nothing for a few moments, then suddenly spotted the twister when it came into view less than a mile away. It seemed to stretch forever up in the sky, and even in the distance he could see the vehicles and rooftops spinning around in and out of the funnel. He ducked for the basement, then came out, jumped into his red chief's car, and was able to dodge the debris and reach the Convenient Food Mart.

Pitching in with the rescuers there, he began to organize the overall rescue operation through the pumper cab radio. Learning of the desperation up on the 422 strip by radio, he drove through the debris toward it, through the downed electrical wires that he knew were no longer a hazard with the power cut off. He passed scores of flattened houses to reach the plaza. Shadow Ridge development: gone. Pepper Tree Lane: gone. Lantern Lane: gone. So devastated was the scene that he thought he had lost his bearings.

The Top of the Strip Roller Rink worried him most. Friday was a big night there for the kids. One hundred or two hundred of them were sure to be there. Huge I-beams and a broad, open ceiling—an invitation to disaster. Had any of the skaters arrived yet? Half the town would have a son or daughter there. And the new nursing home. He wasn't quite sure if any of the elderly occupants had yet been installed.

As he approached the intersection of Route 422 and the Niles–Vienna Road, he could now see the site of the three large buildings that had once stood so proudly there. Chief Semple could think of only one way to describe what he saw: Each of the sprawling buildings had been hit with a giant fly swatter.

Police Officer Bernie Profato shared two things with Chief Charley Semple. One was his devout attachment to softball—he traveled all over the world giving clinics on the game—and a capacity for facing tragic scenes and accidents with calmness and courage. Profato was driving south on Route 46 when it happened. He saw an enormous black cloud in the direction of Niles, and his first thought was that the Reactive Metals Company was on fire. They worked with titanium, and that could mean real trouble in a major fire.

He speeded up to check the problem and then realized that the cloud was moving, sweeping across Route 422 right over the Niles Park Plaza and its companion buildings. He drove faster and reached the plaza to find it a deep mass of rubble. Huge I-beams were bent into pretzels. From beneath came cries and screams of the injured. It was impossible to tell how many there were. Cars in the parking lot were piled on one another, or somehow lifted to sit on top of the rubble. The buildings were squashed so flat it seemed that there was no room under them. Other rescuers soon arrived, along with Profato and Semple and Hughes, and the grim search began, inch by inch through the massive wreckage.

It had all happened so quickly at the plaza. John Lyden, co-owner of the roller rink, was just getting ready to open his doors for the flock of young people who were to arrive within the half hour. Dick Cole, manager of the Thornton Service Center on the corner by the rink, was servicing a few customers, along with attendant Zearl Spillman. Youthful Tracy Stalnaker was getting ready to teach her aerobics class at the plaza building, but only three students showed up because of the generally bad weather warnings they had caught on the radio. Al Segreto was at work in the same building at the Trumbull County Private Industry Council. Elaine Italiano and her husband, Joe, were in their car driving toward Chieffo's Restaurant on Route 422, on their way to the annual spring dinner she had planned for the elementary-school faculty. She had recently received a major award for excellence in the teaching profession.

It was Al Segreto who noticed the lights in his office blinking, three times in a row. He was prompted to go to the opposite side of the building when the roar came and he dropped to the floor. Trapped under a pile of debris, he could hear others screaming and moaning. It was only with the greatest of effort that he was able to extricate himself and turn to help others crawl out.

Tracy Stalnaker was about to cancel her aerobics class, but agreed with her students that as long as they were there, they might as well go through with it. When the lights flickered and went out, they saw the twister through the window. It was heading straight toward them. Tracy, who had recently been studying elementary meteorology, knew the inevitable was to happen. She herded her class into a back room and told them to cover their heads, pulling one recalcitrant lady with her. Then the building crashed around them. The roof above them was ripped off. Debris started raining all around them. Suddenly a car crashed down where the roof had been, landing on the walls that still held up around them. It actually shielded them from the direct suction of the storm.

At the gas station, Cole and Spillman grabbed their customers bodily and shoved them into a small storage room filled with soft drinks, beer, oil, and cigarettes. They escaped injury.

Across the street, a roof of a house lifted and soared over to the plaza. There were three elderly people in the house. They, too, were lifted and whipped through the air across the strip, to crash into the plaza ruins. One body was severed in half, decapitated, dismembered. The others were buried in mud and debris, where several others already lay dead. The cars in the parking lot became pancakes. One car was spun in the air from a mile away and landed at the plaza. Another spun up from 422 and soared over the utility poles to land hundreds of yards away. Joe and Elaine Italiano, continuing their drive on Route 422 to their festive dinner at Chieffo's, were picked up in their car and smashed down four hundred feet away, behind the plaza. Elaine was killed. Joe was severely injured. Though all the doors were locked from the inside, they were found outside the car.

This was the scene that greeted Chief Semple, Officer Profato, Lieutenant Hughes, fire fighters Crockett and Rinaldi, and all the other emergency crews who fought their way through the debris to reach the plaza. They worked with meticulous care. A dislodged timber or beam or cement block could spell the end of hope for an entrapped victim. Many were impossible to find under the debris. Again, the gas was escaping from broken mains. Some electrical wires at this location were still live and sputtering.

With this threat, so much gas was filling the area that the search-and-rescue work had to stop for an hour until the mains could be found and shut off. The trapped and injured faced an agonizing wait.

The scenes were horrifying. One woman lay in the debris with a splintered piece of a telephone pole impaling her to the ground. Two stunned youths were sucked out of their car along with its windows. A woman lay with her scalp torn off, so deeply in shock that it was hardly bleeding. The rescuers braced themselves against their own shock—facing the tragic scene, working desperately to help, trying to comfort the wounded and dying, frustrated with the delay caused by the gas. They, along with the sufferers, were facing what was called "fireman's burnout."

The rescuers turned their attention to an elderly woman and her middle-aged daughter. The older lady was jammed down among the scattered groceries, her arm over her head in a grotesque position. The daughter was clinging to her. "She's my mother," she kept repeating. "She's my mother."

Crockett could not persuade her to let go of her dead mother's hand. He begged the daughter to release her grip, and she finally did. Gently he passed her out of the wreckage to other rescuers. A doctor suddenly appeared out of nowhere. It seemed that almost every bone in the mother's body was broken. She was declared dead. Crockett covered her gently with a torn piece of cloth and turned to search for any other victims.

They had no time then to count the only frail blessings: The few people at the roller rink were safe; none of the kids had yet arrived. The Autumn Hills Nursing Home was still empty; patients had not yet been admitted to the structure, now a nonexistent tangle. The frustration was that no one knew exactly how many were caught in the fury at the plaza—or elsewhere in the path throughout the town.

But at least nine were dead in the plaza complex, and an untold number were injured. County and Youngstown ambulances and EMT crews, called in from a distance, had to detour, fight their way through clogged and almost impassable streets. Ironically, all the local ambulances in Niles had been sent northward to try to help the disaster across the Pennsylvania border at Atlantic, thirty miles away. It seemed inconceivable that an even stronger killer tornado was going to hit Niles over an hour later: after the Atlantic disaster.

The critical, basic problem continued to be frantic, desperate communications, with major trunk lines down and the radio channels jammed. At the plaza, the radio in the cab of Engine Number 4 was chattering with an unbroken stream of messages, most of them impossible to respond to in the face of the Herculean rescue efforts being carried out.

To attempt to bring order out of chaos, Chief Semple dispatched Lieutenant Hughes back to the main fire station to set up a command center. Here the new map came into yeoman service, where locations could be exactly pinpointed and whatever help there was available dispatched to them.

There was the McKinley Heights section, the Shadow Ridge development, the Pepper Tree and Lantern Lanes devastation that had to be dealt with with whatever forces could be organized and dispatched. The rescue teams had to take one building at a time, check it, try to account for all the people who might be in it, report back, then turn to another building or what was left of it.

With fragmented facilities, the command post was not easy for Hughes to set up. Again, the ham radio network came in to fill the critical gap as the phone service battled against fallen lines. Three operators set up at the main fire station, calling in help and dispatching information to the county disaster officials, sheriff's department, Highway Patrol, and road and relief crews. Along with the entire fire and police departments, the hams would be working through the night and all the next day. There was, in fact, little sleep in Niles that night—or in any of the other towns to the north that had been stricken.

Still, very little news from Albion, Atlantic, Newton Falls, or Niles had leaked through to each other. The call that had pulled the ambulances of Niles toward Atlantic was an exception. The radio dispatchers were able to reach them and call them back to Niles from several miles away.

Those towns that had been hit seemed to find it hard to believe that anyone else could experience such disintegration, that Nature itself would have any force left to expend on other communities.

Yet gathering even more momentum, the maxitornado that had brought such devastation to Niles was continuing to move eastward toward the border, toward Wheatland, Pennsylvania, barely twenty miles to the east and with only a few scant broadcasting warnings to indicate that incomprehensible destruction lay ahead for them as it had for its neighbors.

11. / CROSSING THE BORDER

The thick, turbulent funnel roared toward Wheatland, just to the north of U.S. 80 and parallel to it. It was merciless, wide as four or five football fields were long, never lifting from the ground, and like the other giant killers, choked with heavy shrapnel. Where there were no tornadoes, there were damaging winds, hail, heavy rains, and lightning pummeling the countryside—most of this springing up swiftly and with little indication in the sky.

It was those violent thermals rushing up through the thunderheads that were creating the havoc—those that were rising because they were less dense than the air above them. Because the jet stream aloft was rushing eastward above the massive supercells at a speed faster than the surface front, the giant warm bubbles were smashing into the cool air of the jet stream, vertical wind shear being created. At eighteen thousand feet, the jet stream rolled the weaker winds near the surface, causing them to spin like a lumberman rolling a log under his feet. The rolling surface winds were pulled into the supercell and sucked upward. As they did, they tilted on an angle. The vertical wind shear then whirled the spinning air faster, tilting it even more toward an almost straight up-and-down cylinder. The faster the rotation in the thunderstorm, the more likely for a tornado to develop. In fact, the longer the spinning lasted and the more violent the spin, the greater was the expectation for a tornado, shooting up from a 60 percent chance to a 90 percent chance.

An endless succession of severe-storm warnings continued to be issued by the Erie, Cleveland, and Pittsburgh weather stations—and from the crippled Youngstown facility indirectly through the others whenever a fragmented phone message could get through. There were so many weather statements being issued, in fact, that the commercial broadcast media were hard put to keep up with them. Many were missed, and the listening audience was far below that for the prime-time segments. Further, "severe storm" warnings lacked the immediacy of tornado alerts, and listeners gradually became sated with them in spite of the awareness efforts the weather service had been continually promoting.

On the TV news at six, just about an hour before the killer tornado was crossing the border toward Wheatland, there was talk of a possible tornado touch-down far to the west, at Ravenna, Ohio—and also at Jamestown. But the weather had brightened in Wheatland, and everything seemed calm. Most assumed that the worst must have passed on. At 6:45 P.M., Youngstown was able to get a brief phone message through to Pittsburgh about a possible tornado development in the Wheatland area. Pittsburgh passed the alert along minutes later, but there were no spotter reports or hook echoes to back it up with a full warning. At 6:55 P.M., the Cleveland weather office picked up a ham radio message that a tornado had touched down at Newton Falls, but added that this was only speculation. Five minutes later, the same ham operator confirmed the touch-down. But by that time, the tornado was moving with such speed that Niles had already been hit.

The town of Wheatland sat in the Shenango Valley, dotted with sprawling industrial plants with varying degrees of prosperity, most of them on the down side. Some were fairly robust, like the tubular products division of the Cyclops Corporation, which had two plants in action there—except that they were on strike at the time. Wheatland Tube also was active, along with the Sharon

Steel Mills, the Yourga Trucking Company, and others in an industrial area that had seen varying fortunes over the years. Wheatland belied its name. It was no longer a place where you could tickle the ground with a hoe. It was a cluster of smokestack industries clinging to industrial hope in a computer tech age. The old Erie Canal once brought thriving commerce to the town, in sharp contrast to the big trailer trucks that pass the town by in the distance on the turnpike. The Shenango Hotel downtown typified the old days of the traveling drummer, in contrast to the Sheraton a few miles out of town, near U.S. 80.

Mayor Helen Duby lived with her husband up on the hill that overlooked the town and valley. She was a gracious lady, well loved and respected, with a calm outlook on life and quiet strength. She had been mayor for eight years. Her major regret was that she had never been able to finish school. She came from a farm family of fifteen children and came to visit a friend in Wheatland over forty years ago. She met her husband at that time and has lived in the town ever since.

She had spent a busy but uneventful day. At the town hall, she listened to a few citizen complaints, talked to members of the city council, signed a few papers, and arrived home in late afternoon for an early supper with her husband, recently retired from his job at the National Casting Company. Her husband helped her do the dishes as they talked affectionately about their two married daughters, one in Kentucky, the other a receptionist for a local physician.

At about seven that evening, she was sitting casually at her sewing machine while her husband was in the living room watching TV. He was one of the few viewers in the area who saw a crawl with the severe-storm warning moving across the screen. But they had seen this so many times before in the past. Most of them had been false alarms, and they reasoned that this undoubtedly was in the same category. Outside, the weather didn't seem particularly threatening, although the sky was beginning to darken.

Mayor Duby went back to her sewing. Not long after, she heard a slight patter of hail against the windows. She crossed to them and looked out. They were just about the size of mothballs and did not seem too alarming. She was about to continue sewing, when the clatter of the hail increased. She went to the kitchen door. She was surprised to see that the size of the hail had increased measurably. They were now fully as big as golf balls. She called her husband to look at them. As she did, she heard what she thought was the rumble of a group of jet airplanes.

"Wonder where all those planes are coming from?" she said.

"They're not planes," her husband said as he looked out. The sky had suddenly blackened. "That's a tornado. Get down to the cellar."

They ran. The noise rose to unbelievable decibels. The sound seemed to fade in a matter of seconds. Then there was a deathly silence. They stayed in the cellar for a few minutes more, not knowing what had happened or what to expect.

When they came up, Mayor Duby rushed to the front door and looked down over the valley. "Oh, my God!" she yelled out. "Wheatland's gone! There's absolutely nothing left!"

From her doorway, the town looked as if a steamroller had ground down over it. There were no landmarks she could make out. There seemed to be no streets, no poles, no homes, no crossroads. Only factories, most of them flattened to the point of being unrecognizable. The sky had suddenly cleared to a calm, bright blue.

She was gripped by a feeling of unreality. Her home was unscathed. How could it be that an entire town lay in the valley in a carpet of ruin? All in a matter of seconds? She was thinking: The town is my home—and that is destroyed, even though my house isn't.

Almost in a trance, she got in her car and started down the hill toward the town center, toward the Municipal Building—if it was still there and if she could find it. All the people on her street were milling around outside their houses. They appeared to be in a state of shock.

"What's happened?" a neighbor called to her in disbelief.

The mayor slowed down and called, "I don't know myself. I can't believe this."

She was thinking: This is a thing that can't possibly happen to us, to our town. It simply can't happen. She passed other neighbors. No one was hurt. There was no damage on the hill. This added to the unreality.

Down on the town level, she found it hard to get her bearings. Landmarks were gone. The Shenango Hotel was nowhere to be seen. Nor was the Valley Baptist Church. Miraculously, the Municipal Building was still there, next to the untouched firehouse. Down the street, the Security Systems Company also was untouched.

As in the other stricken towns, people were walking around in a daze, like zombies. Some shouted to her incoherently. She was unable to stop; she had to organize, to call for help from the outside. It was not easy to ignore them, but she pressed on. At the Municipal Building, the power and phones were out. Here she learned that the only two private ambulances were on their way to Atlantic to help there, just as had happened in Niles. Somehow they were contacted by radio and called back. Meanwhile, Chief George Keryan and Fire Chief Andy Clark were summoning all the help they could get in the county by radio; their staffs already were starting out to find the trapped victims. She pressed on to the Security Systems building to call the utility companies first. The gas leaks and electrical wires were everywhere a clear and present danger. Then more calls to the Emergency Management Agency, the National Guard, and the Army Reserve unit in nearby Sharon.

A car was useless in most areas. Mayor Duby rushed out on foot to survey the scene quickly. There were cries and screams from unseen people under their houses. She passed a man sitting by a car. No one was near him. He begged for help. She lifted him with all her strength to some porch steps that were still standing. He died in her arms as she did so.

Soon volunteers gathered. From the cries, many were trapped in their basements. A team would form, dig under the wreckage with bare hands. One member stayed to take care of the trapped, while the others moved on to the next house. A woman got out of her car and ran to the mayor, crying that she wanted to get to her home. Mayor Duby had just passed that home; she had to tell her that there was no home to go to. Another woman came screaming to her that her son and grandson were trapped in the cellar. Mayor Duby tried to calm her down until a rescue team reached there. My God, the mayor was thinking, what can I do for her? Please, God, what can I do?

She fought back displaying the agonized emotions going on inside her: I'm in a situation where I'm not allowed to show my emotions. I've got to live by a double standard. I can't let myself even look tired from now on in. God will help me to have the strength to go on.

Just at that moment, a woman came up to her and said: "Has anyone given you a hug yet? I think you need one!"

The mayor hugged her back. She felt new strength.

Twenty-seven days before Mayor Duby stood among the utter ruins of her town, former mayor, former councilman, and former fire fighter John Goda gave his daughter Yvonne away in marriage. It was a festive affair, especially so because Yvonne and the bridegroom, Dave Kostka, were briskly active in the community and almost inordinately popular. Both worked as postal carriers, which is how they met. Together they had so many friends that the wedding church was hard put to handle the guests.

Thirty-six-year-old Dave Kostka loved life, children, sports, and the outdoors with zest and passion, and of course joined in the springtime softball action in every capacity, from player to umpire, from Little League to adult league. In 1980, Kostka won the Bob Hoffman Sportsmanship Award of the softball association, a high honor in the community. Living near deer hunting country, he would go hunting in the season with so many others, but solely for his supply of meat for the year. Often he would get down on the ground and explain to the deer why he shot it. His enthusiasm for everything he took hold of was contagious; it was the prime source of his popularity.

John Goda, a burly and affectionate man, loved Dave Kostka almost as his own son. He was so proud of him that he was fond of showing the wedding pictures to everyone who had the time to look at them, and he was waiting for the proofs of more pictures that were due to arrive from the professional photographer any day now.

At five-thirty on the evening of May 31, daughter Yvonne came home with the news that Dave had been asked to umpire a Little League game, and his little niece Christa had begged him to take her with him. He would be back home right after the game.

With the Westinghouse plant in the valley closing, Goda was waiting for a civil service appointment on May 31 and was enjoying the chance to do some chores around the house. Taking a break, he flicked on the TV set to catch the evening news when it came on. At that time, the crawl was moving across the screen with a mention of a tornado watch in the area. But again like so many others, he paid little attention because nothing had materialized in the past, and there was no mention of a warning.

A little later in the news, the weather commentator mentioned that there were unconfirmed reports of tornadoes to the west of Wheatland in Ohio, and also up in Erie and Jamestown. Goda listened attentively, but his reaction was that now all the bad news was over and everyone could relax. The weather still was clear, and Goda was sure the storm must have passed them by.

Then the small-size hail began to patter against the windows, hail that soon rose to a clatter as the size increased. By now the sky had darkened, and his young son John came into the room to say that the weather really looked rough. Having been in a small tornado several years before, Goda decided to take some preventive action. He told his wife and son that they all might as well go down to the basement for a bit until the storm passed over.

Goda gathered some flashlights and a few blankets, and the family went down to the basement in a mood of relaxed precaution. After a few moments, Goda decided to go back upstairs again and look at conditions. He went out the back door to the lawn and looked to the west. The sound began to rise "like hundreds of engines." Yvonne emerged from the cellar and grabbed her father by the arm to pull him downstairs again. Goda was convinced that all they were experiencing were heavy winds.

The noise stopped after less than half a minute, and still he was convinced that the worst had simply skimmed by with little damage. He emerged again from the cellar, and all was bright and clear. Nothing around him seemed to be damaged. Then, for the

121

first time, he looked downhill toward the town. The three-story Hotel Shenango was simply missing. It wasn't there. Neither was the Sawhill plant. There had been a row of some fifty houses near it. He counted them. There were only nine left standing, and most of them were on a rakish angle. He scanned the whole town area. Wheatland was gone.

He yelled for John to get the chain saws and gear together. Then Yvonne came running out of the house.

"Dave's down at the ball field! What's happened to him? Is he safe? What's happened to him?"

She was in tears. "Don't worry," Goda said to her. "Dave knows what to do in a case like this. You don't have anything to worry about." She continued to sob.

Then, as he stood far up on the hill from the town, Goda heard the hissing sound from the gas escaping from the big steel plants down below, from both broken steam pipes and the gas main. Goda and John jumped into their truck and headed down for Church Street in the main part of town.

A tornado with the force of F-5 had never hit Pennsylvania before. Since 1940, the region had experienced only twelve violent tornadoes. The highest on the scale was F-4. Further, the three killer tornadoes that had struck between five and seven o'clock that late afternoon and evening had not followed the flat terrain generally associated with tornado alleys. They were smashing across sharp hills and later mountains farther to the east, confirming the fact that such terrain could not block or break up their fury.

Adding to the savage destruction was that an epidemic of tornadoes had developed, tornadoes with strong downbursts as well as the vicious suction. Even in traditional tornado country, epidemic tornado families and F-5 giants were not common. The biggest outbreak in history took place in April 1974, when 148 tornadoes hit thirteen states from Alabama to Michigan. Over three hundred people were killed, and six of the twisters reached the F-5 force. One of them struck Xenia, Ohio, where a half-mile-wide swath was cut through the town. Another hit the village of Guin, Alabama, where a state trooper radioed a report: "Guin just isn't there." Or in nearby Jasper, where a broadcaster reported: "We can't talk to the police department—it just blew away."

This was the state of Wheatland when Goda and his son arrived at the mass wreckage of the town. But less than half an hour before, Dave Kostka had picked up his seven-year-old niece, Christa, in his Chevy Blazer and arrived at the Little League field in his dark blue umpire suit ready to officiate, and hoping that the weather would hold off for the game to be played. When he arrived about forty people had gathered, determined youngsters and passionately enthusiastic parents who would be rooting more strongly than if the Pittsburgh Pirates were by some magic playing in the World Series.

A light spray of rain delayed the start, during which time Kostka discovered that ten-year-old Keith Scott had no means of getting home that evening. Kostka reassured him that he would drive him home, and prepared to start the game as the rain suddenly let up.

Kostka had barely called "Batter up!" when one young player pointed to the west. The funnel was coming directly toward them. Someone shouted, "There's a lake inside it!"

Kostka took command. He yelled to the spectators to grab the kids and dive for the dugout. He herded them inside the low concrete structure. There was barely room to hold them all. Then Kostka snatched up his niece and young Keith, dumped them into his Blazer, and drove off to try to dodge the twister in any way he could, and help his mother to safety at her home.

He turned left, on the road by the Yourga Trucking Company. As he did, the tornado veered from its course, headed directly toward him. The Blazer rose in the air, then smashed down. Kostka pulled the children out, threw them into a ditch, and lay down on top of them. His vehicle lifted in the air, soared across the street, and smashed into the side of the trucking company.

As he tried to protect the children with his body, the whirlwind ripped him away from them. He sailed high in the air and smashed against the collapsing wall of the trucking company. He died instantly, half buried by debris.

The wind began lifting little Christa from the ditch. Keith grabbed her ankle and held on with all his strength. The fury passed by in seconds more. The children were dazed and bleeding. They began wandering about in total confusion. One of the few townspeople who was able to move a car in that area saw them. He rushed them to the hospital.

Less than a block away, Goda was bringing all his experience as a fire fighter to bear on the search and rescue efforts. Someone yelled to him the news that everybody at the ball park was safe. A surge of relief came over him. There was turmoil everywhere. He helped dig out a man on Church Street and found him alive. Then he and young John turned to the next house, where a grandmother was trapped with two grandchildren. She was moaning and could respond to their questions with grunts only. They seemed as if they were coming from the cellar. Later they found that her voice had been carrying along the space between the joists. She was actually crushed between the fallen walls and the joists. By the time they reached her she was dead, but her grandchildren were safe. What Goda didn't know was that in moving from house to house, he passed directly by the half-buried body of his son-in-law several times.

Goda kept working on adrenaline as the National Guard arrived with floodlights. He found strength he never knew he had. At ten-thirty he returned to his home to get more equipment and to see if his son-in-law had come back safely. A call came in from Dave Kostka's sister. She had found her daughter, Christa, at the hospital. She was injured but safe. Little Keith Scott was there, too, with broken ribs and badly ripped skin. The hospital had told her that Dave also had been there and had been released. Everybody breathed in heavy relief. Knowing Dave, John Goda thought, he was as hard at work in the rescue efforts as he himself was.

Goda went back downtown to the endless rescue work. The body of a salesman was pulled from the totally destroyed Shenango Hotel. Everywhere he went, Goda asked the crews if they had seen Dave. No one had. He came across an EMT ambulance driver and asked him the same question. The driver evaded his eyes. "Yeah," he said. "Dave's dead."

Goda lost all control. He grabbed him by the collar and screamed, "No! No! No! That can't be true!"

"You better ask the firemen over there," the driver said.

Goda grabbed the fire chief and spun him around. "Is that true? Is it true Dave is dead? Tell me that's a lie."

The chief nodded. Goda went haywire for a moment, then collapsed. Gently, the firemen took his truck keys away, put him in the chief's car, and drove him home. Yvonne saw them carrying him in. She thought they were bringing Dave home dead. She went into hysterics and collapsed.

Christa's father, Kenny Wallender, was there and he grabbed the phone. He called several hospitals to see if Dave had been admitted, dead or alive. At the hospital in Sharon, a town close by, he was told they had five bodies, but no identification for any of them. There was, however, one body that was almost unrecognizable. He was wearing a dark blue umpire suit. There was a baseball and a strikes-and-balls ticker indicator in the pocket. There was no question now: Dave Kostka was dead.

Patrolling along Interstate 80 eastward of Wheatland, Corporal Tom Carr of the Pennsylvania State Police stopped to help a stranded woman driver near Milepost 6. He was wondering why he had not heard any radio dispatches from the Mercer barracks, about fifteen miles east of Wheatland. As he got out of his patrol car, he looked at the sky. The tornado was approaching Mercer. He grabbed the radio mike to report to headquarters. There was no response. Electric power was off over nearly all the county. There was no way for the headquarters desk to call out—nor for any of the disaster centers to spread warnings except by battery radio.

To the north on Route 18, Paul Bortz was driving in his '82 Dodge pickup, listening to WWIZ-FM in Mercer. At exactly 7:07 P.M., announcer John Borelli was repeating the news of the tornado watch, just after the regular newscast. Bortz listened intently. But halfway through the report, his car radio suddenly went off the air. Attempting an instant repair job, he banged hard on the dashboard. Nothing happened. The station was dead. A heckuva time for the station to stop broadcasting, he was thinking.

When the power went off at the WWIZ studio, Borelli and salesman Vince Nelson could do nothing but sit in the light of a Coleman lantern. The phone was working, and Borelli turned on the answering machine, noting the time of 7:12 P.M. He left word for whoever called to call back when the power went on. But shortly after, they saw the twister coming straight toward them, two hundred yards away. They dove for the floor in the control room. Borelli looked at his watch. It was 7:22 P.M. What time am I going to die? he wondered. Nelson noted the time, too. Mentally he began to compose his own epitaph: "At exactly 7:22 P.M., Vince Nelson met his death on May 31, 1985. . . ." He prayed at the top of his lungs but couldn't hear himself talk over the roar. Then it subsided. All the outside walls were gone. The two-hundred-foot tower was a pile of twisted spaghetti. The house across the road was simply gone. So was WWIZ—except for the inside walls that saved their lives. Just beyond the radio station, the twister suddenly lifted and disappeared back in the belly of the supercell.

Production Manager Jeff Wimer's baseball game had been canceled, and he had gone on to the graduation ceremony directly. When he got back to Mercer later that night, he still had heard only vague rumors of tornadoes. He put in a phone call to the station. He could hear it ringing—but with no answer. It was ringing deep under a pile of cement blocks and rubble. Then the station manager's wife called: "WWIZ is totally destroyed." Wimer got in his car and drove through rubble and fallen trees to reach the station. At a roadblock, the National Guard let him through after he showed his press pass. In the light of a full moon, the station looked as if it had been through a holocaust. Wimer broke down and cried.

12./*DEATH AT THE SHOPPING MALL*

By 7:30 P.M. four main killer border-crossing twisters had gouged their way eastward from Ohio through Pennsylvania, up to fifty miles in length. There was only fragmentary communication among the stricken towns and villages. Rescuers were too busy digging out the injured, the maimed, and the dead, clearing paths through trees and utility poles that had been splintered like toothpicks. As darkness approached, no one knew how many were missing, who was entrapped, who was dead. Towns that had not been stricken and had heard the piecemeal news were certain that the worst was over. From Wheatland up to Lake Erie, sixty miles away, the storm was gone but the agony wasn't.

Forty miles to the south of Wheatland, the National Weather Service at Pittsburgh was at 7:15 P.M. yet unable to confirm any local "ground truth," and to dispatch a tornado warning over the crippled public communications system for the local counties. But at 7:45 P.M., an ominous severe-weather statement went out of the teletypes and radio weather wire:

> MOST OF THE SEVERE WEATHER THIS EVENING HAS
> OCCURRED OVER NORTHERN PENNSYLVANIA . . . BUT

THE STORMS WILL BE MOVING INTO THE SOUTHERN
HALF OF THE AREA WITHIN THE NEXT FEW HOURS. . . .
SOME OF THESE STORMS WILL CONTAIN LARGE HAIL
. . . DAMAGING WINDS . . . DANGEROUS LIGHTNING
. . . HEAVY DOWNPOURS AND POSSIBLY TORNADOES.
BE ALERT AND READY TO TAKE COVER.

As if to demonstrate the fragmented communications throughout the whole of western Pennsylvania, the dispatch added:
THERE HAVE BEEN SEVERAL UNCONFIRMED REPORTS
OF TORNADOES THIS EVENING. To the north, the tornadoes
had already been tragically confirmed on the ground.

Beaver Falls and North Sewickley, Pennsylvania, the twin
towns just a score of miles to the northwest of Pittsburgh, had
scarcely heard any news about the tornadoes. Few had seen or
heard the latest warning from the National Weather Service at
Pittsburgh. Carl Mosketti was neatly wrapping a bottle of Gallo
wine for decorator Gladyce Brenson at the state liquor store of the
Big Beaver Plaza. A few stores down, Jess Megaree, the visitor
from Lancaster, was standing outside the Jamesway Department
Store to meet his father-in-law, who had called to say he had
arrived there. The Spotlight 88 drive-in theater was ready to
receive Chief Dale Sutherland's son and his classmates for their
graduation celebration at the intersection of Routes 65 and 588.
It was shortly after 8:00 P.M.

Megaree phoned back to his relatives to find that he was waiting at the wrong Jamesway store. As he started walking toward
his car, he heard the roar. Then he saw the funnel. Then he saw
several cars lift up, spin, and crash into the roof of the plaza. One
blew by him in the air. He forced open a Jamesway door, made
a baseball slide inside next to a counter, and covered his head.
The roof of the entire building ripped off above him. The steel
beams bent like rubber. The ceiling crashed down. He was buried
under debris. He prayed, "Lord, please let this pass." Bruised
and bleeding, he lived. Later, dozens of blouses and dresses, still
with Jamesway price tags, were found miles away, stringing
from the branches of trees.

All but one wall of the state liquor store was ripped away. Both
Mosketti and Gladyce Brenson were crushed to death. Along the

shelves of the remaining wall, bottles of Johnnie Walker, King's Ransom, Jack Daniels, and Gordon's gin sat in neat rows, untouched and undisturbed.

Minutes before, Chief Sutherland was sitting at home watching TV. His wife had gone to visit her sister, and he was alone in the house. Moments later, the firehouse called to say that a tornado had been spotted to the west of town. Sutherland didn't think too much of it; there had been so many false alarms in the past. But the next call reported that the twister had touched down.

Not too alarmed, Sutherland started out through the kitchen toward the cellar door. He looked out the window. The sky was black. As he opened the cellar door, the window burst into a thousand pieces. Then the back door blew open and blasted him off his feet. He was pulled by suction down the cellar steps. Out a cellar window, he could see a twenty-eight-foot-long I-beam. It began to peel off and then was wrenched away, his garage and patio with it. The kitchen cabinets were embedded with glass, but Sutherland was not cut.

He looked out the window again toward the intersection of Routes 65 and 588. The black whirlwind was just approaching it—the butcher shop, the service station, the hardware store, the Spotlight 88 drive-in. Then it hit. Every structure exploded. When the dirt and debris cleared, the intersection was literally flat. It looked as if nothing had ever been there. Thank God, thank God, Sutherland thought, the kids were not yet at the theater. The big metal projection booth, wider and heavier than a ranch house, had cut a hundred-yard path through where the cars and the schoolkids would have been parked.

Responding with other volunteer firemen, police, and volunteer rescuers to the scene at the intersection, Sutherland found three entrapments at Ken's Butcher Block, another at the ticket booth of Spotlight 88. Injuries were severe, but the death toll everywhere was unknown. People were stunned, walking around in a daze, in circles, some screaming, some crying, some mute. Sutherland along with many other rescue workers everywhere throughout the stricken region would be working without sleep over the next three days.

But the twister did not stop at Beaver Falls. It continued onward to the east, crossing the major arteries of U.S. 76 and U.S. 79, sweeping into Butler County, crashing into a Tupperware party as it did so. Eight ladies rushed for a root cellar outside the house. All but one were successful. She was found dead in a stream some two miles away.

The funnel approached quiet Evans City. It veered slightly to the south, sparing the town but heading toward John's Bar and Grill at the top of the hill just outside town. By now, the bar was packed with its early weekend patrons enjoying a beer or a Scotch or a boilermaker. Waitress Dorothy Pitts had just taken an order in the family dining room and headed for the kitchen when she heard a late arrival yelling that a tornado was sweeping across the fields directly toward them. Some fifty people at the bar hit the floor in seconds. The diners in the other room dove under the tables. Dorothy Pitts slid under the bun rack in the kitchen. The roof lifted, the front portico spun away, the ceiling came down, the pipes burst and flooded the rooms with water. Rising, she watched the funnel take half a house across a field and away up the road. Miraculously, no one was hurt.

But in Beaver Falls, and in all the other stricken towns, high schools were about to become morgues. Churches, fire stations, and town halls were becoming shelters, free cafeterias, information centers, food and clothing distributors, and emergency medical and psychiatric centers. An area as large as Massachusetts and Connecticut combined was reeling under the impact of five giant killer tornadoes, plus a total of thirty-six others almost as deadly, including several in New York and Ontario. The battle between the relentless air masses that finally confronted each other had created a blitz and war zones that were hard to comprehend. And as in war, the innocent were the ones to suffer the most.

13. /THE COMING OF DARKNESS

Sunset came at 8:48 P.M. in the region where the tornadoes raked across the towns and landscape of Ohio and Pennsylvania. The paths left deep gouges and scars that ran as long as 140 miles. Some were over two miles wide. In the towns that bore the brunt of the attack, the scenes were much the same. Portable generators with floodlights swept across houses and buildings that were barely recognizable. Desperate friends and relatives sought the missing, the dead, the injured, the trapped. Sirens wailed nearby and in the distance. Caravans of ambulances and police cars wove through and around fallen trees and poles and even houses sitting in the middle of the street at rakish angles. Everywhere was the high-pitched screech of chain saws in the attempt to clear lanes in hopelessly choked roads, to give a final *coup de grâce* to toppling buildings, to free timbers from those still caught under the wreckage. Homeowners clawed through the splintered remains of their houses, blindly seeking family treasures, papers, jewelry, photographs, pets, and toys.

Hardly anyone slept that night. Nearly every able-bodied resident pitched in to aid in rescue, clear debris, or feed the volunteer crews that formed almost immediately. Many worked through the night and even through the following night and day. The National Guard was swiftly mobilized and dispatched to town centers, along with police, fire, county, and state disaster teams, the Red Cross, the Salvation Army, highway and utility departments, doctors, nurses, EMTs, and local church groups. Fire companies and equipment arrived from over twenty outside communities.

With the coming of darkness, no one knew the final toll in death and injuries, to say nothing of property losses. Confusion still reigned; communications still were shaky and intermittent. In Albion, Mayor Bonda Dahlin declared a full state of emergency at 8:00 P.M. and set a 9:00 P.M. curfew. Barbed-wire barriers were stretched across damaged areas, and only emergency vehicles were permitted to pass. The mayor's husband, Borough Councilman George Dahlin, took over as disaster coordinator, leaning heavily on a quickly assembled team of volunteer ham radio operators. They remained the only links with the outside world.

In the previous year, local Red Cross chairperson Martha Sherman had completed an arrangement with the junior high school to set it up as a disaster center. She had also held a meeting many months before with the local emergency management and fire department officials to delegate responsibilities in case a major emergency arose. She had no idea that the planning would be brought into use so forcefully and so quickly. At least the readiness would now pay off.

As soon as she arrived at the school, the relief operation went into action. Medical teams arrived to set up a triage station and treat the injured. Ambulances from Erie Hospital wailed in to take the severely injured there. Food supplies began to flow in as if by a cosmic signal. Private cars drove up, packed with everything from baby food to adhesive tape to sanitary napkins.

As Martha Sherman worked in dim lanternlight with calm efficiency to organize the various relief departments and procedures, a friend approached her and called her aside.

"I'm afraid to tell you this, Martha," her friend said, "but Debbie is dead."

Martha could not quite take in what she meant. "Which Debbie?" she asked.

"I'm afraid it's your Debbie. Debbie Sherman."

"My Debbie is gone?"

Martha's eyes brimmed with tears. She half succeeded in choking them back. "Thank you for telling me," she said. "This makes our work all the more important, doesn't it?"

She turned back to her job. She worked all through the night and the next day without letup.

Editor Bob McClymond of the *Albion News* knew he had the biggest story in the history of the town, but he could hardly face writing it. He felt guilty that he and his family were alive and unharmed, when his neighbors' lives had been monumentally shattered. He worked with the rescue crews to extricate as many as he could. It took about two hours to do so. One neighbor was dead. Others were injured.

But the whole impact didn't sink in until he walked through the town with his wife to realize the extent of the damage. The storm was so selective. Total obliteration in one part of town, totally unscathed in others. The news office was in perfect condition; the path of the storm missed it by two blocks. So were the home and family of meteorologist John Halfast, who worked all through the night shift at the Erie airport without news of their safety reaching him.

McClymond took his news photos with a heavy heart until dark, then drove to a neighboring town to call his relatives to let them know that he and the family were safe. His ninety-year-old aunt answered the phone, and he told her, "Just want to let you know we're all fine."

"Oh," his aunt replied pleasantly, "that's nice." And she hung up on what she interpreted as a cheerful social call.

She had no idea yet what had happened. Nor did many others throughout the region as they continued to remain in the dark, even when only a short distance away.

Nightfall brought no peace elsewhere. A full count of the casualties was impossible. Families desperately sought missing loved ones. Others refused to leave the piles of rubble that once had been their homes. Chain saws continued to whine all through the night. Dogs and cats wandered aimlessly to try to find homes that no longer existed.

Dawn came on Saturday morning at 5:52 A.M. A strange sight was seen crossing the border from Ohio to Pennsylvania. The silhouette of a long caravan of frail, black horse-driven carriages was seen moving along the road toward Jamestown and Atlantic. The wagons were packed with food, grain, hammers, saws, clothing, treadle sewing machines, and sturdy Amish and Mennonite farmers coming to the aid of their brothers—and anyone else—who needed help. Nearly a thousand more would arrive by bus and van from as far away as Wisconsin, Michigan, and other Amish-Mennonite communities throughout the country. But they created only one of many visible symbols of what members of all churches, all creeds, all sects, all businesses, factories, stores, and suppliers were doing: springing into action in a surge of spiritual dedication to help others.

This marked the beginning of a new wave, a new invasion of a region that had been crisscrossed by Indians, Colonial soldiers, pioneers, industrial strife, and the ravages of Nature. With the new wave would be an emergence of faith and spirit that seemed to be as powerful as the force of the tornadoes that had been so merciless. There was anguish and desperation, of course. But the counteraction in human resiliency was to reflect the hidden springs of man's better nature.

As editor McClymond wrote in his paper:

> At 5:15 on the night of May 31, the Albion News was confronted with the biggest story in its 85 year old history. I didn't realize it at first.
>
> The full extent of the death and devastation wasn't clear until early Saturday. Twelve residents of our community died in the few seconds it took for the killer tornado to sweep across Albion, our neighboring community of Cranesville and parts of two adjoining townships. More than 200 were injured and some 160 families left homeless; over 140 in Albion alone.

Nearly one third of the homes in this little town of 1,800 people blew away. The tornado was a top story nationally. A veteran Red Cross Disaster Team member later told me it was the second worst disaster he had ever seen. . . .

Our little town has been seriously hurt: the wound is deep and painful. But it's not fatal. The spirit of the community as expressed by residents and community leaders is nothing short of miraculous. Words and pictures are totally inadequate to describe what happened to our town on May 31. Words are equally inadequate to describe the fantastic spirit of cooperation that has marked almost everything that has gone on since that fateful hour. The generosity of folks from all over the country has been overwhelming.

It was, and is, a horrible experience, but it has had its gratifying moments.

Our town will be back. We will rise again.

McClymond was speaking for all the towns that suffered the same shocking devastation that Albion had. So did two announcements in his classified section of the paper:

Words are inadequate to express our grief and the thanks we wish to convey to all who assisted in our recent tragedy. Knowing that the paramedics and many volunteers were doing everything within their power is a comfort. Thank you all so much.
The family of William Revak

I would like to send my undying gratitude to my brother Rick Fehr for saving the lives of my children and myself. I don't know how long I lay under the rubble of my home. Just as I thought death would have me, I heard your screams. Thank you Rick for saving the lives of Kelly, Amanda and myself. Love you. Janet.

Poignant were the letters of the third-grade pupils of the Elk Valley School near Erie when they learned that a three-year-old boy was seriously hurt in a nearby hospital. Nine-year-old Renee Lucas drew a picture of a head and a rainbow and wrote: "My dad worked eight hours for three days rescuing people and cleaning up everything on the ground. His name is Mike Lucas. My name is Renee Lucas. I care a lot! I sure hope you're going to be okay! My mom donated money, but I'm going to take some out of my wallet and donate some. I'm thinking of you and I'm concerned.''

Another classmate wrote: ''I hope you get better. You don't know me. I'm still thinking of you. People are giving money, food and clothes. Hope I see you sometime. . . .''

Still another wrote: ''Even though I don't know you, I care about people who are injured. Get well soon. Mom and Dad are helping to clean up.''

Whatever the generation, the concern for others was springing to life everywhere.

14. /*THE WAR ZONES*

In Pennsylvania, an editorial in the *Meadville Tribune* caught the atmosphere of hope in the midst of ruins:

> There are hundreds of personal horror stories in the wake of Friday's tornado disaster. Paths of destruction will resemble war zones for some time. But among all the misery, there are good things too.
>
> An underlying story of this catastrophe has been one of compassion. People helping people.
>
> Hundreds of volunteers, many thankful that their own homes and families were spared have been working around the clock to help victims in every imaginable way. Many are assisting on a one to one basis while others work through agencies and service organizations to aid those with storm losses.
>
> The Bill Brown family is among the hundreds whose homes were blown away Friday. Pausing briefly during the cleanup work, he summed it up this way: "You don't realize how good people are until something like this happens. They can't do enough for you."
>
> Heartwarming variations of this statement have been heard countless times amid the outpouring of help. Even total strangers are

giving of themselves and are making some of the greatest positive impacts on the lives of weary tornado victims.

In Ohio, similar thoughts were echoed in the *Youngstown Vindicator:*

Everyone who survived will divide his life in parts before and after the tornadoes that devastated vast sections of the area. It will be what Pearl Harbor and President Kennedy's assassination were to earlier generations.

For many the shock and fear from the explosive winds' horrible destruction will stand out in the cruelest light. It couldn't be any other way. Personal tragedies in loved ones lost and homes destroyed are the ultimate memories.

But another memory will stay with them with only slightly less vividness. That is the tornado of help that swept in quickly after the tornado of destruction left.

The entire area became one community, a community of concern, a community filled with the desire to wash away the pain afflicting its members, to help the stricken regain their normal lives.

It was a nobleness of spirit replying to the brutal vagaries of nature. The display of good will and caring became a comfort to us all.

The headlines that greeted the citizens of the region on Saturday, June 1, were grim. TWISTERS SMASH AREA; MANY DIE; HUNDREDS INJURED splashed across the front page of the *Youngstown Vindicator* in letters two inches high, with the story going on to say: "Exact figures on the number of dead and injured were not available this morning, as authorities struggled to dig out from the debris. They were still finding bodies as they searched through the rubble. Governor Richard F. Celeste toured the most devastated portion of Trumbull County shortly after midnight and declared it a disaster area. . . ."

The New York Times gave the story a front-page, column 1 position, but none of the papers was yet able to count the dead or assess the damage.

*   *   *

It was ironic that back at the National Severe Storms Forecast Center in Kansas City, the confirmations of their own forecasts were slow in coming in. So swamped were the local weather offices that they had little time to send back information, and because of the chaos and confusion of the "ground truth" areas, few details were leaking through.

Fred Ostby didn't learn about the potential terror that had struck the Ohio Valley until about nine on Friday night. The news came back to Kansas City over the wires in fragments. Much of it was unconfirmed. Printouts were scattered: Albion, 12 dead, 82 injured . . . Atlantic, 23 dead, 125 injured . . . Wheatland, 7 dead, 60 injured . . . Beaver Falls, 9 dead, 120 injured—and that twister was rated only F-3, in contrast to others at F-4 and F-5 . . . Niles, 10 dead, 250 injured, with a maximum F-5 force. Some figures were right, others inaccurate.

There were few details coming into Kansas City. The worse the tornado, the less the news. Local fire and police only a block or so apart were having troubles of their own learning what their colleagues were doing. But sketchy as the information was, Ostby was shocked at the violence of the storms he and the Severe Storms Center had predicted as early as three o'clock Friday morning, with the decision to dispatch the tornado watch at four twenty-five that afternoon.

In retrospect, Steve Weiss's geographic calculations were uncanny in their accuracy. Weiss, whose shift ended at 4:00 P.M. on May 31, went home to greet visiting relatives. It wasn't until the next morning that he picked up the paper. His mouth dropped open when he read the headlines. For the first time, he learned about the devastation that had taken place in almost the exact locations he had pinpointed. Although he had expected severe storms and had issued the tornado watch, he was shocked at the intensity.

Along with Fred Ostby and the others at the center, he reviewed the charts the next day. Here the areas hardest hit had been circled the previous day. The question on both of their minds was: Did we do everything we could? The markings on the

139

chart indicated that they had. The problem was that from eight hundred miles away they were fighting against a grotesque enormity of Nature that could challenge any instruments man could yet devise, even when the computations were correct.

Even the local stations of Cleveland, Youngstown, Erie, and Pittsburgh, a handful of miles from the capricious funnels, were hard put to compete in the race with time when the twisters dive-bombed out of the skies. Unlike the clumsy, cumbersome, and weaker hurricanes that at least were unable to hide or to spring out of nowhere with a sneak attack, the tornado remained the ultimate challenge. There was literally no way they could be stopped. There was no way the hideous mass destruction could be avoided. There were, however, plans for development of ways to save human lives, but they would be of little use until the following decade.

In the spring of 1985, there still were gaps—gaps in knowledge and gaps in instrument improvement that would be taking place in the coming years. Ostby was looking forward to the time when improved forecasting numerical models would be installed that would provide accurate information where squall lines would fall, where sudden changes in stability and dew points and temperatures and dry lines could be anticipated, all on a smaller scale.

There was a grave irony attached to this. High-resolution Doppler radar, already past the development stage, had been around for half a decade. Since it can measure how fast the precipitation is moving toward an area, and the velocity of the wind in which the raindrops are embedded, an advance warning of up to half an hour would be possible. However, several federal budget cuts over the previous few years had seriously delayed the program.

Charles Hosler, a meteorology professor at Penn State, and past president of the American Meteorological Society, took note of this after the tornadoes had struck. ''Those of us who are in the business and have seen this Doppler system work feel there is a terrible, unnecessary loss of life occurring all over the country,'' he commented. He was not alone in his opinion.

Still, the ground spotters would continue to play a critical role where human eyes had to be counted on, where meteorology left off and human alertness came in. At the Cleveland National Weather Service office, Marvin Miller reviewed his actions and those of his staff and concluded they had done everything possible under the limitations they had to live with. Specifically, they needed more volunteers like Clayton Reakes, who over the years had been willing to spend hours of fruitless watching from his post on the roof of the city hall, yet had come through with the critical warning that had unquestionably saved lives in the town of Newton Falls. In spite of the savage F-4 and F-5 forces there, not one fatality followed in the wake. Reakes later was to receive a public service award from the National Weather Service ''in recognition of service contributing to public service and welfare.'' He was also to receive similar awards from the Ohio State Senate and the U.S. Congress.

There would be criticism forthcoming, of course. Raymond Camp, chief of a volunteer fire department near Albion, told the press: ''There was never any warning that we heard. When we were digging people out, that was a comment that I heard over and over—that there just wasn't any warning.''

But the Erie weather office had posted a tornado warning for Erie County at 5:13 P.M. This was two minutes before the tornado had touched down in the town. Of course, there always was a lag before radio stations could get the warning out, and few people had the NOAA radio channels that would have brought them the news more swiftly. The problem was that some people were getting the warnings and some weren't. And of those who did, not many took them seriously. In Erie, Bob Sandstrom continued to have a feeling of frustration, because they had done everything they could there, and still the casualties were high.

At the Pittsburgh office there was the same frustration, with the added complications of having to cover Youngstown's territory along with their own. Even after the Beaver Falls tornado had gone by. Bill Drazl was keeping his eye out for a possible tornado invasion of Pittsburgh itself. ''There's nothing sacred protecting a city like Pittsburgh from tornadoes,'' he commented. ''There's no wall around Allegheny County.''

Ray Visneski, his colleague, agreed. ''Only the darkness of night spared Pittsburgh,'' he said.

Fortunately, after nearby Beaver Falls had been stricken, the warm, moist air near the surface had cooled, and with it the upward rush of the columns of boiling, unstable air was slowing down. At 9:40 P.M., however, a funnel cloud was sighted less than ten miles from Pittsburgh. But it never touched the ground.

Forecaster Bob Wieder at Erie reasoned that the violent river of air of the jet stream sweeping more to the south than usual contributed greatly to the severity of the storm system, along with the collision of the two air masses. He commented: "Two air masses fighting each other, that's what it was. They were having a war between themselves and taking it out on someone else."

During all the time the twisters raged through the region, the meteorologists had no chance to observe the scenes on the spot. They were cloistered against the elements. Their instruments told them that all hell obviously was breaking loose, but they were unable to see and feel and experience what was happening. Dave Bell left the weather station at Erie and drove to Albion, where the scenes that greeted him were shocking. The next day, he flew in a light plane to follow the track of the vicious tornado that had leveled Atlantic and then moved on toward the east.

After it left the more populated sections it headed for the Allegheny National Forest, strewing shingles, papers, clothing, road signs, bankbooks, and other debris from up to seventy miles away all along the path with it. For the first time, Bell was able to observe the track that stretched continuously from the Ohio border eastward in a straight line.

A giant rotary power mower could not have cut a cleaner path through the thick forest that began at Tionesta. Looking out the windows of his plane, Bell at one point counted eight different parallel tracks, plus one main swath that had contained a multiple-vortex funnel that gouged out a trail nearly three quarters of a mile wide at certain points. The twisting of the fallen tree trunks—large oaks and maples—revealed the violent spiral action of the winds.

Although the population here in the mountain woodlands was more sparse, the anguish was no less apparent. The entire population of the county was barely five thousand. In the small community of Tionesta, seven people were killed. The injured had to be carried down steep mountainsides on stretchers. The winding mountain roads were hopelessly clogged. Over four hundred homes were leveled, some of them held for five generations by families. Dead cattle and deer were sprawled over the countryside.

Later, timberland destruction was to be estimated at over ten million dollars in the thirteen thousand acres that were almost demolished. It would cost over half a million dollars simply to gain access to the damaged areas. Nature had spared neither itself nor man, nor the sense of frustration among the forecasters.

There were many strange happenings in the wake of the tornadoes. In Albion, Ted and Barbara Podoll were away from their home when it was demolished, but their dog Pepper was home. When they returned, he was missing and they gave him up for dead. Hours later, they heard him whining under the wreckage and were able to pull him out safely. The refrigerator inside the ruined home of Clark and Janet Snodgrass sailed a quarter mile away and ended up on the roof of a bank. A two-year-old baby was whisked away from his mother's arms and was nowhere to be found. Minutes later he rose up out of a ditch, safe and unharmed, but with all his clothes stripped from him. A utility pole was found dangling twenty feet up in a tree. A splinter was sticking through a stainless-steel pan. A broomstick pierced a utility pole.

A farmer's dog was tied to a tree. Both the tree and the dog disappeared after the tornado went by. Three days later, the dog was found in a field, still tied to a piece of the shattered tree trunk. The dog lived. Parrots and parakeets suddenly showed up in people's yards, with no immediate way to find and identify their owners. Checks, letters, old-time photographs, and clothing were found up to fifty miles away from their origin.

Nine-year-old Carmella Fennell was talking on the phone with her parents, who were away in San Diego on a business trip. Suddenly the mother heard her daughter scream, "Mummy, something is wrong! It's going to be a hurricane!"

143

Then Mrs. Fennell heard Marie Gratta, the seventy-two-year-old baby-sitter, cry out, "It's coming! It's coming!"

Then the phone went dead. Mrs. Fennell, with little Carmella and two younger children at home, spent half the night desperately trying to reach her home or neighbors in the face of downed telephone lines. Hours later, she was successful. She learned that her baby-sitter had rushed the children to the basement and thrown herself over them. A neighbor, Jeff Armstrong, dug them out, while his own infant nephew and two neighbors were killed. The Fennell house was demolished. Both parents prayed with thanks all the way back on their flight home.

A hundred miles to the east of Niles, Ohio, a couple in Clarion, Pennsylvania, picked up an envelope. The return address was the Niles Monument Company, which had been ravaged at the same time the cemetery next to the firehouse had been ripped apart by the twister.

In one of the few cases of looting reported, a couple routed some trespassers at gunpoint, then experienced expansive generosity from total strangers. An unidentified donor dumped two full truckloads of new lumber by their destroyed house to help them rebuild. Another family, strangers also, sent them the house keys to a log cabin nearby to use as a temporary home.

Actions like this began to become commonplace. The *Erie Morning News* not only created a massive food distribution operation with the help of local businesses but also served as a clearinghouse for offers of free housing to the displaced. Column after column of listings appeared with such notices as:

Mary Schaefer, 9915 W. Ridge Road, Girard has a large home with two twin beds, two cribs, a double bed and a sofa bed available.

Thomas Kauffman, 636 Benson Road, Waterford, has a bed in a house and a camper trailer that can hold up to eight people.

Jack Stetson, 5575 Meehl Road, would offer shelter and could also handle livestock.

Shelly Liebline, 7541 Fairfield Road, could handle two people in beds and others in sleeping bags.

144

Robert Christensen, 760 West Melhorn Road, Fairview, offers a
bedroom and a couple of sofas.

Terry Schnepp, 3936 Essex Ave., offers a spare sleep couch and
an extra mattress.

Hundreds of offers of this nature flooded the newspaper office,
so many that the publishers had to shut down the donor list and
accept only calls from those who needed the shelter. In addition,
food donors swarmed into the paper's offices. Their contributions
filled several large semitrailers provided by local industries, to
the extent that additional food had to be transferred to other relief
agencies. It was beginning to appear that the storm of assistance
was becoming more than equal to the storms of destruction.

The outpouring of aid was evidenced elsewhere. A dog-food
company packed its large semitrailers with human food and turned
it over to the stricken towns. Grocery stores and fast-food chains
emptied their shelves without charge. Hardware stores did the
same. Motels opened their doors to the homeless, along with
churches, schools, and other public buildings. There was practically no looting. Two towns in France cabled Albion with messages of sympathy. The towns of Albion, Michigan, and Albion,
New York, phoned to offer aid.

In Beacon Falls, Connecticut, over three hundred miles to the
east, volunteer fire fighters Mitch Mulinski and Bobby Cole were
sitting around the firehouse reading the paper, along with Chief
Harold Lennon. They came across the story of what had happened in the town of Beaver Falls out in Pennsylvania. Well over
a decade before, their own area had been hit by a tornado centered in Waterbury, and the memory of it still lingered. But the
Pennsylvania tragedy appeared to be much worse.

The chief suddenly said, "Beaver Falls sounds a lot like Beacon Falls. Why in the hell don't we do something for these
guys?"

Mulinski and Cole immediately agreed. Just what they could
do, they didn't quite know. But ideas began to shape up fast.
The fire chief at Beaver Falls could not be reached, but a phone

call to the police chief there indicated that the firehouses in Beaver Falls and North Sewickley were attempting to feed a thousand people a day and that they would welcome any kind of assistance.

Bobby Cole, a natural-born salesman, got on the phone and contacted several leading businessmen in the town and managed to persuade them to donate a thousand dollars to help the cause along. Several other calls brought in about two thousand dollars' worth of food, including a donation from the local Nutmeg Bakers' Supply of forty-two cases of cookies, twenty-five cases of juice drinks, and several hundred pounds of flour and sugar that added up to nearly five hundred pounds. Adrian's Kitchen, a local diner, threw in several dozen sandwiches, and the nearby Peter Paul Cadbury company flooded them with candy bars. The men of the fire department had just received checks from the state for fighting a local brush fire, and the entire company endorsed over its checks, earmarked to their fellow firemen in Pennsylvania to start their children's toy collections over again.

By local word of mouth, people arrived with other donations, including over two hundred jars of baby food from the Klardiaf Grocery. Meanwhile, Chicoski's Market arranged for the purchase of cases of canned corn, peas, cereal, spaghetti, sauces, and other nonperishable items through his wholesaler at cost. U-Haul donated the use of a sixteen-foot box truck, while Mulinski, with a disabled bad back, and Cole drove it around the town to fill it nearly to capacity. Although the trip would take twelve hours each way, Mulinski insisted on going along in spite of his back.

From the conception of the idea to the takeoff for Beaver Falls took just twenty-four hours. They left in their firemen's dress uniforms at 8:00 P.M. Monday evening, and drove along U.S. 84 to U.S. 80, to arrive twelve hours later, on Tuesday morning.

In the chaos and confusion of the rescue efforts, the police department had failed to notify the Beaver Falls fire chief of the pending arrival of the Connecticut men. As the U-Haul truck pulled up to the fire station, the chief greeted them in stunned surprise. Tears filled his eyes. He told Mulinski and Cole that the greatest damage to homes and people was across the river in

North Sewickley, and jumped into his car to lead them to Chief Dale Sutherland there.

Driving through the wreckage of homes and buildings, the Connecticut firemen could not believe that people could have survived the storm's fury. On the way there, Mulinski was stung with the views he saw: an automobile rolled up like a piece of tinfoil; a house leveled to its foundation, with an American flag stuck into a mound of rubble; bulldozers demolishing half-destroyed homes, children playing in the wreckage. Almost in the center of the rubble was Chief Sutherland's fire station, a stone's throw away from the intersection of Routes 65 and 588. It was miraculously untouched. Cole thought it looked as if God had taken a crayon and drawn a circle around the firehouse to say, "This is going to be the disaster center. Don't touch it." The ladies' auxiliary there was in the process of serving meals at the rate of seven thousand a week to homeless, rescue workers, and utility repair crews, and was hard pressed to keep up with the pace.

Chief Sutherland sent Mulinski and Cole into the station to have coffee and breakfast and to lie down on cots while his men unloaded half the truck at the fire station and the other half at the school disaster center. Inside the firehouse, Cole saw a hundred or more men, women, and children having breakfast there. Within minutes, he saw the kids drinking the canned juices they had brought. That alone seemed to make the trip worthwhile.

The kids were taking the disaster lightly, Cole noticed; perhaps they didn't understand how bad the situation was. The older people appeared to be philosophical, bitter but ready to rebuild and get on with the job. It was the young adults who affected Cole the most. They seemed to be standing around in wonderment, asking themselves, "What the hell do I do now?" Cole dozed off on his cot for a brief nap with the wish that they could have brought ten more truckloads. Mulinski's back was hurting badly. He claimed he didn't mind it at all. They drove all night back to Connecticut.

15./NO DOORS TO LOCK

Sunday morning was grim in the region. Families were packed into the homes of relatives or friends; some were camping on cots in the hastily improvised disaster centers. People were almost in a dreamlike state, poking through the ruins to find treasured family memorabilia, valuables, special missing toys, or pets.

In Albion, Sandra Stahlsmith and her husband, Bill, returned to the wreckage of their home, still in shock from the loss of little Luke. Looking at the ruins, Sandra could not imagine how she or any of the children still lived through the ordeal. Most of the house had fallen into the basement. The family pastor of the non-denominational Grace Fellowship in Erie had taken the Stahlsmiths in, where they would remain until they could obtain some kind of permanent housing. With the image of Luke indelible in her mind, she dug through the rubble to try to find anything salvageable. But there was little that could be: a few clothes, some blankets and pillowcases, some towels. "I want to live for the sake of my other children," she said. "This was not God's work. It was the work of Satan." She was firm in her resolve not to cry in public, but when she was alone, she would burst into uncontrollable tears.

Nearby, a child was crying for her Cabbage Patch doll. The father raked through the rubble and finally emerged with it, a triumphant smile on his face. Over on Park Avenue, Linda Quay tried to salvage what she could from her home, at the same time stopping to pick glass fragments out of her scalp.

In another part of town, a hundred worshipers met at Albion's Grace Methodist Church, where the minister stated firmly that the town would rise again. "We will reach out," he said, "and embrace all in need. All of us are victims in the ultimate sense. When one weeps, we all weep."

With his church unharmed, he meant what he said. The church became a distribution point for the entire town. Bedding, shirts, blouses, sweaters, slacks, and shoes filled the Sunday school rooms to overflowing. Instant potatoes, canned soup and vegetables, spaghetti and spaghetti sauce, and cereal jammed the church kitchen for anyone in need, without cost. One of his parishioners whose home had been completely wiped out said, "We didn't lose everything. I've got my children and my husband. All we lost were sticks and nails."

The St. Lawrence Catholic church in Albion still had chunks of plaster falling from the ceiling and glass falling out of the windows. Several Protestant churches offered their buildings for Masses to be held.

In Atlantic, it was estimated that over eighty homes had been destroyed. Hundreds of tree stumps, black and ugly, reached toward the skies with shattered limbs, brown and leafless. Many were totally felled and lay in twisted, ugly spirals in a half-mile-wide swath.

The Congregational church was set up as the disaster center, and picnic tables were set up both in and outside the church. The Red Cross had already moved in and set up the kitchen; later the Mennonite Disaster Service took over. The two trailer trucks from Dad's Dog Food were already in service, one of them supplying much-needed refrigeration. Food poured in from surrounding communities as volunteer workers set up the kitchen. They would be feeding over a thousand a day.

Reverend Polley arrived early for an ecumenical church service. In spite of the bent chalice and the gaping holes in the roof, he held communion services. He knew what the theme of his sermon would be. Hadn't he found the Bible open to the Book of Job? If ever the patience of Job was needed, it was at a time like this.

"Job was human as we are," he spoke. "He got angry. He complained, and he asked why terrible troubles were happening to him. Just as a lot of us are asking today."

He also said, "We have to have a vision. We have to look ahead. We have to rebuild, we have to face it. We are now walking through a deep valley, but God is with us."

And to lighten the hearts of his congregation, he spoke of Job's eventual reward for his patience, whereby the Lord granted him fourteen thousand sheep and several thousand camels, oxen, and donkeys. "But don't forget," Polley concluded, "he only allowed him one wife."

Reverend Polley was gratified to find a contagious, cheerful spirit among the relief workers as well as the townspeople. It seemed to transcend the overwhelming tragedy. There was also the ecumenical spirit that emerged. Within a day, Polley's church joined with four others in the area to set up an organized relief effort. They in turn joined hands with the Amish and Mennonites, and a fusion of all creeds and beliefs took place to help surmount the overwhelming damage of the storm.

As he spoke, an Amish woman arrived in her carriage at the church. Her home had been destroyed. But she brought in steaming casseroles and cinnamon buns to the church kitchen.

Across the border in Niles, Ohio, Reverend McCutcheon surveyed the ruins of the parsonage and wondered how she and her husband could possibly have survived the storm. She remained steadfast to the creed of her church: God can do anything. In her hand was a check for one thousand dollars. It came from the Catholic church in town.

In neighboring Newton Falls, the First Congregational Church stood roofless. Over the front entrance was a sign, WITH THE FAITH OF A MUSTARD SEED WE CAN MOVE MOUNTAINS.

Back over the border in Wheatland, Pennsylvania, Mayor Helen Duby told the press, "We desperately need state aid. I'm going to ask for the moon. But I'll settle for half a moon."

151

Meanwhile, the relatives of David Kostka were preparing a hero's funeral. Later he would receive a posthumous award for heroism from the Pennsylvania State legislature.

It was many days until the final toll in death, injuries, and property damage was assembled. Counting the tornadoes that hit Canada the same day, eighty-eight people were killed and over a thousand injured. Property damage in the United States alone came to half a billion dollars. In Pennsylvania the impact of the storms was unprecedented. There were sixty-nine fatalities. Nearly a thousand homes were destroyed, over twelve hundred damaged. Along with industries destroyed, the state's losses came to over a quarter billion dollars. In a single day, Pennsylvania suffered more deaths than the total of all the tornado fatalities recorded in that state since 1916. It was estimated that if all the wrecked and damaged homes were to be rebuilt, the construction would equal all the new homes built in the stricken areas over the previous three years. So many utility poles were fallen that a phone company official commented, "This will be like rebuilding an entirely new phone system from scratch." The 312-foot AT&T relay tower in Atlantic lay like a crumpled skeleton on its side. It had carried thirty-two hundred circuits that now had to be replaced or rerouted. The major lesson: Killer tornadoes can occur anywhere in North America, city or country, plains or mountains. No region was exempt.

The force of the twisters surprised officials as they began to appraise the damage. They wondered how anyone could have remained alive in the paths. In Niles, Lieutenant John Hughes meticulously counted the damage. Sixty-two single-family homes were obliterated, along with twenty-one apartment units and the unbelievable crushing of the steel frame buildings of the Park Plaza compound. Nearby, three giant propane storage tanks weighing seventy-five thousand pounds each were lifted up, crushed like Dixie cups, and tossed across a road. In Wheatland, corrugated steel roofs of several factories were draped around trees, poles, houses, and fences in sizes and shapes that looked like crashed airliners.

Pennsylvania Governor Richard Thornburg, visiting the area on Saturday, lost no time declaring it a disaster area and requesting federal funding from the president. The governor summed up the reaction of everyone who viewed the scene for the first time. "The area must be seen to be believed," he said. "We use the word 'awesome' from time to time, but I think there is no other way to describe what the forces of Nature have done. Industrial facilities with structural steel bent out of shape like straw. Whole areas flattened as if they had been carpet-bombed. It's indescribable."

He was speaking in Wheatland, where 95 percent of its industry had been wiped out. Here, the Sawhill Tube Company had no offices left for its employees to come to. They were told to stand by until a temporary office could be set up. The Wheatland Tube Company, one of the few to escape damage or ruin, promptly donated $150,000 to the town and the flattened Baptist church.

On Monday, President Reagan declared the area eligible for federal disaster funds. "I commend you all for your tremendous courage and resilience," he said. "These storms are among the worst in decades, and have clearly taken a heavy toll." On Tuesday, Vice President Bush was slated to speak at a Republican fund-raising dinner in Pittsburgh. He detoured his flight to the Youngstown airport and drove in a cavalcade to Wheatland.

He said he was impressed with the guts and courage of the people, and he promised swift action in federal relief. "It's awfully hard to understand the force of something like this until you see it," he added. Mayor Duby later commented, "I think with the governor being here and with Vice President Bush following him up, I think it will be the rebirth of Wheatland. I believe with all the helping hands, we will be lifted again."

But the federal and state funding was not the flow of manna from heaven, although eventually funds would be available for everything from food stamps to temporary housing to low-interest loans. At just about the time the U.S. Senate was voting to fund $38 million for the Contras in Central America, the Stateside victims would be receiving sluggish assistance for their own recovery. And as Secretary of Defense Weinberger was privately objecting to the investigation of the purchase of $436 claw hammers, $7,000 coffee makers, and $640 toilet seats in the military budget, the government was balking on supplying temporary home trailers for farmers in Pennsylvania. Rhonda Brooks, a public-affairs officer for the Federal Emergency Management Agency, told reporters rather stiffly, ''When the president declares a disaster, the gates of Fort Knox do not open, and mobile homes do not start to be moved down the streets. We will deal with this case by case, in an orderly manner.'' She was responding to local officials who were being pressed by people living in tents, and farmers who were trying to contain loose cattle in fields strewn with deadly pieces of glass, metal, Fiberglas, or wilted leaves forming deadly prussic acid, any of which could easily kill livestock.

As could be expected, applying for aid was a difficult job. Many were without cars and had to travel miles to crowded facilities, where overworked staffs were attempting to deal with anguished families still in shock. The process was awkward. Papers required were deeds, utility bills, driver's licenses, insurance policies, estimates of losses, and other documents. Some would travel great distance to discover they had forgotten to bring essential evidence. Others made fruitless searches through the rubble of their homes to discover that papers and documents had disappeared and perhaps blown miles away with no hope of recovery.

Evidence of this sort of long-distance scattering continued to come in. A sign from Pymatuning State Park reading DO NOT LITTER BEACH was found fifty miles away in a town that had no beaches for miles around. Farmer Lyle Bisbee watched the whirlwind take away his new barn, and with it seventy head of prized cattle—several of which were never found. A man twenty miles to the east of Albion found a chunk of insulation in his yard wrapped around a canceled check written by his own mother thirty years before.

With so much property destroyed, the towns themselves faced monumental problems. Property damage in industry-heavy Wheatland mounted to fifty million dollars. Albion, with less industry, suffered over thirteen million dollars, equal to more than one third of the town's tax base. Local officials wanted desperately to offer tax relief and refunds. But with the tax base shattered, they could only turn to the state, which in turn was matching federal funds for relief and reconstruction. In Atlantic, with people losing all their property, the local taxes had just been collected, but to return refunds would financially wipe the town out.

In Albion and elsewhere the immediate problem was cleanup. As Mayor Bonda Dahlin said, "I can't be concerned with figures and tax bases right now. What I'm interested in is getting Albion cleaned up, in getting our people back their possessions, and helping them every way possible."

Cleanup was, of course, urgent. Without it, the towns would remain paralyzed. The search began to find dumping sites equal to the job of handling the tons of debris safely. In some cases, parts of public parks had to be sacrificed. Fire breaks had to be constructed to guard against spontaneous combustion. Bulldozers dumped enormous loads of splintered timber on trucks to be hauled away and burned. So many piles of two-by-fours, roofs, shingles, and siding were being burned that the towns were choked with acrid black smoke, adding chemical tears to the genuine. Meanwhile, scores remained in hospitals, and as many businesses were losing business with power out and roads still blocked.

The economic impact of lost jobs in the crippled factories could not be estimated. In Niles, a General Motors plant had been moving at an accelerated pace in the face of new demands. It had a two-shift operation set for the day after the storm. Only twenty-five hundred of eight thousand workers showed up, and they had to be dismissed.

In the face of all the chaos, many of the insurance companies did a remarkably good job. Adjusters were on the scene as early as Saturday morning. Some were able to issue checks immediately, most of them being cost-of-living coverage while the major replacement estimates were being worked out. In some cases, with a house fully destroyed, the entire payment of the insurance coverage was issued on the spot. Metropolitan Insurance set up special emergency procedures, with a toll-free number and an increased grace period. No policies were canceled for nonpayment of premiums.

There were problems. Many policies required that mortgages

had to be paid off first out of the insurance settlements. With whole blocks in ruins and people scattered, adjusters had trouble finding policyholders. Many policies did not cover tree damage unless the house was struck. Cleaning up large trees and shredded stumps cut off like matchsticks could amount to heavy cost. Major damage claims came from cars ruined by hail, as well as those crumpled into tin cans. The hail, up to the size of baseballs, brought unbelievable and practically total damage to cars.

People had to be warned sharply about returning to their damaged or ruined homes. They not only had to be on the lookout for live wires, but even broken lines could suddenly spark to life in a surge of power. Checking for gas leaks as well as turning off main switches was a critical step before entering a homesite. Householders were warned to keep freezers closed, that full freezers would keep food better than partially full ones. Doubtful food with odd color or odd odor should be thrown away. Dry ice was advised to save the frozen foods, and people formed long lines at the Carbonic Products Company, which sold it.

What settled over the distressed land was an ambience that people found hard to delineate. National Guard Private James Kerr, of Company C in Erie, a stock clerk in the Giant Eagle Supermarket, arrived on duty in Albion and put his feelings quite simply: "I really feel like I'm doing something worthwhile here." Except for keeping an eye out for outsiders and curiosity-seekers, the National Guard found its duties light. In the quiet town of Atlantic, one local resident said, "I don't think you'll find three people here who lock their doors at night." Many, of course, now had no doors left to lock.

Unexpected needs arose constantly. Scores of people could not find their eyeglasses. The Northwest Pennsylvania Optometric Association offered free pairs to all who needed them. Many complicated engineering problems were sprouting up. The Society of Civil Engineers offered free technical assistance where needed. Volunteers working through the night needed food, often after some of the relief stations were closed. Food was left outside for them. The floors of firehouse and school relief centers were packed with so many cartons and grocery bags full of food that there was barely room to walk among them. Clothes were neatly sorted, marked for size and ages, and freely offered to all who requested them.

"It's hard to explain what has happened," Reverend Mc-Cutcheon said at her church in Newton Falls. "All the religions and denominations seemed to fuse in one ecumenical whole. It seems that there never was anything so bad that God couldn't make something good out of it. People everywhere have grown closer together. A positive attitude has emerged in the face of the catastrophe that I've never seen before."

Surveying the devastation of Atlantic, a county sheriff shook his head sadly. "This was always a fairly poor community," he said, "so I don't think many people plan to stay on—except the Amish." Nearby, an Amish teenager was telling a reporter, "You just have to grin and bear it. We'll just rebuild, that's all."

These appraisals reflected the mind and mood of these frugal, God-fearing, Devil-hating, hardworking Pennsylvania Germans. The two things that counted most to them were God and themselves. They carried no insurance. They would refuse government help.

Bishop Yoder summed up the situation succinctly: "One reason we don't accept government assistance," he commented, "is that we get it done faster this way. Most of the barns have to be done before too long for the grain and hay and cattle. We figure to begin them as soon as possible. And when something like this happens, we call in Spartanburg, Punxsutawney, Trouville, Middlefield, New Wilmington, Mercer—we all get together. Some call it a bee. We call it a frolly. Everybody brings eats, and we all go to work."

They did allow some assistance on a modest scale, but only after they made sure others were taken care of first. There was a desperate need for clothing, and they accepted donations of cloth, all of it in the traditional dark colors of black, navy blue, or dark green. The women in their long dark blue dresses and white bonnets worked feverishly at their treadle sewing machines to fill the need.

The reaction of the Amish and Mennonites to the disaster

brought a sense of amazement to all who had a chance to observe it. The caravan of frail carriages that plodded its way toward Atlantic at dawn on Saturday morning was no unorganized accident. It was part of the long-standing tradition that the Amish and Mennonites resolve to put aid to others as a priority above any other. The first caravan was only a harbinger of what was to follow later as Amish and Mennonite assistance was to flood into the region from as far away as Wisconsin, Delaware, North Carolina, New York, Minnesota, and elsewhere.

They came under the aegis of the Mennonite Disaster Service. As an international organization, it was set up to help people everywhere when disaster strikes. Both Amish and Mennonites are dedicated to responding to the needs of their fellow men regardless of their faith or beliefs. In the small leaflet that the Mennonite Disaster Service hands out when they arrive in a community, they state, "We may be strangers to you but you are our neighbors. We cannot fully understand your loss but we want to share your burden. We consider anyone in need our neighbor. When disaster strikes we desire to give assistance as we are able. There's going to be a lot of work."

Bishop Yoder would later go on to bury Andy Byler in the tiny Amish cemetery in Atlantic. He said that the tornado was a sign that God was testing their faith, but that the Amish were bound closer together than ever.

"God is telling us something," he added. "People might not be awake as they should be as far as spirit is concerned. It's God's way, not our way."

Asked how he planned his brief and laconic sermons, he said, "We ask the Lord to put in our mouths what we should say, and speak from within."

There was some advantage in carrying no insurance. Saturday morning in Atlantic found the bearded Amish men with their wide straw hats and bib overalls moving from farm to farm with saws, crowbars, and hammers in hand, already starting to work on reconstruction without waiting for insurance adjusters. Twenty-five Amishmen showed up from Mercer, Pennsylvania, twenty-two miles away. They had hired a van and a driver to bring them up. No one expected them at that time; they just showed up at the Troyer farm with its flattened barn. "We never saw the Troyers before," one of the volunteer group said. "People around here didn't know we were coming. We weren't told to come. All this is quite a mess. We just want to help clean up."

The organization of the relief work on the local scene was simple. The local Amish and Mennonites showed up with their own tools and usually with their own food, and set out to work in a matter of minutes. One Red Cross worker in Atlantic remarked, "These guys are really something. They just show up and work like crazy, and won't even take a cup of coffee. They say it should be used for other volunteers who weren't able to bring their own supplies."

In Jamestown, Harold McCrea, who had seen the killer tornado sweep down the valley from a distance, was almost in awe of the Amish relief efforts. "I tell you, those Dutch are really something," he said. "They might call us the 'English,' but they sure as hell try to help all of us as much as themselves. They're real nice people. You gotta respect their life-style. Our Lions Club here had to beg them to take some money, money to buy themselves spectacles. And clothing. Matter of fact, they did have to turn down some bright-colored stuff—but they did take underwear. And then the other Amish from outside come in here by the busload. From Ohio, New York, you name it, and they go right up one street and clean up broken poles and trees and debris, and start right down another. Stack everything neat, then they're off to another town. Never seen anything like it. Unbelievable."

Disaster was nothing new to the Mennonite Disaster Service, centered in the small town of Akron, Pennsylvania, just outside Pittsburgh. Usually it is known as the MDS. Traveling youth squads, along with senior workers and counselors, are constantly being dispatched to disaster areas for cleanup and rebuilding, working in cooperation with local officials, the Red Cross, the Salvation Army, and other agencies. The MDS workers receive forty-three dollars a month, and their instructions are simple: Keep a listening ear as you interact with a victim; feel compassion as you realize the hurts and losses disaster leaves; sense a greater love for God as you share His love with others.

The volunteer squads are further reminded of the purpose of

their organization: "We endeavor to be a continuing example of selflessness by giving our time, talents, possessions, and energies to help relieve disaster-caused suffering. Be friendly and optimistic, but not so lighthearted to imply the situation is not serious. No task will be too menial. Respect personal property and rights of ownership. Treat victims as equals—don't patronize or slight them."

With the local Amish already swinging into action, the international organization followed close behind. Busloads arrived in the most stricken areas of Pennsylvania and Ohio within the week, over eight hundred workers who swarmed out of their buses, working up a smashed and damaged block and down another, neatly sawing and stacking wood, preparing rubbish for carting before moving on to another town to repeat the operation. Many of the teams came from Lancaster, the heart of the Pennsylvania Dutch country, about two hundred miles away to the east. This rich farm country bred sturdy workers. To manage the double job of keeping their own farms going and helping their distant neighbors, families would split up. Half the workers from one family would go to the stricken areas for several weeks or so. Then they would return to the family farm, and the other half would leave for their shift of relief work. This long-distance shuttle was to continue for weeks and months for many of them.

The MDS separated its work into two functions: cleanup and rebuilding. Cleanup came first, and the ground rules for these squads was that everyone was skilled for this work. They were reminded by the central office that one person's junk is another person's treasure and that every effort should be made to salvage and preserve. Always important was the listening ear. "Victims are still adjusting to the reality they face," their instructions read. "You may be able to help them regain their footing spiritually, emotionally, and physically."

For the rebuilding units, the MDS set a priority in helping the elderly, handicapped, widowed, low-income, and minorities, offering free labor. When the May 31 tragedy struck, the MDS already had teams working in other tornado disaster areas. A caravan of four vehicles with long-term volunteers were hard at work with tools, equipment, furniture, and building supplies in a town named Maxton, North Carolina. Finishing their work there, they were soon to move on to eastern Ohio and northwestern Pennsylvania to continue their work. Busloads would be arriving every two weeks from Lancaster, Maryland, Wisconsin, Indiana, and Canada. As one Pennsylvania townsman put it while watching them pitch into a job: "They might be small in numbers, but they sure as hell have a big impact."

Another Amish-Mennonite delegation was finishing up a restoration job in Barneveld, Wisconsin, after working there since a tornado struck the town in 1984. Although not quite finished, they moved on to the East, where the trauma was great and the need urgent. The new victims they came to help could only shake their heads in disbelief because the relief teams made no distinction between the Amish or non-Amish in their efforts to help. As Amishman Eli Yoder, arriving from Ohio to help in Pennsylvania, summed it up: "It doesn't matter who's Amish or who isn't. I feel sorry for everybody."

Then he added: "It makes you feel guilty to go home again. You have to come back down until it's all straightened out."

Charles Grocé was the local project leader in Atlantic and Albion. He was the one who heard the tornado at Atlantic four miles from his home but did not see it. In fact, he had no idea of its intensity when he left his home to go to a Mennonite Church meeting fourteen miles away, in a different direction from Atlantic.

Arriving at his church, Grocé found no one there and was puzzled. He waited outside until a game commissioner he knew came up with the news that Atlantic had been all but wiped out. He rushed to his car and tried to get through to the town. Most of the roads were impassable, and police cars and ambulances made it almost impossible to reach the center.

When he finally got through he coordinated his work with the Red Cross, assigning Amish volunteers to specific jobs and setting up the local Amish to work with the national disaster workers when they arrived. A hundred days after the Atlantic tornado, Grocé still was working full time at the church center set up in the Congregational church, where workers from every denomination throughout the area were continuing to join hands in the endless work of rebuilding the community. Grocé could not yet take the time to prepare for his photographic exhibit at Carnegie-Mellon in Pittsburgh, but when he felt his job was over, he would do so.

The Amish had no corner on the generosity flowing through the region; they attempted to shun publicity. It was the "English" who were heaping praise on their efforts, almost failing to acknowledge that they shouldered an equal burden of relief work throughout the area.

16. / "DREADFULLY SAD AND REAL"

The tornadoes cut deep, narrow gouges out of the landscape, giant knife wounds that would leave indelible scars over fifty miles in length. They also left deep psychological scars, not only for those living in the narrow tracks of the tornadoes but also among the people who were totally unscathed on either side of the devastation. What emerged in the aftermath was a condition that became known as tornado guilt: Why did we survive and escape ruin when our friends and neighbors were so hopelessly stricken?

There were many different manifestations of trauma among both the afflicted and the unharmed. In Newton Falls, Carolyn Sembach, wife of Public Safety Reserves leader Larry Sembach, found that she could not face going down to the destroyed center of town for two days. It would simply be too painful. She found herself reflecting on the actions of her neighbors whose homes were wiped out while her own home was only lightly damaged. There was something so poignant and pitiful about the neighboring women who came out immediately after the twister had passed, one to sweep her sidewalk in front of her almost leveled home, the other to rake leaves in the face of equal destruction.

There was something both brave and beautiful in these fruitless actions.

Then there was the pride of the people, Carolyn noticed. As they poked through the rubble of their homes, many simply could not bring themselves to come to the relief centers for food. It was too much like begging. They did not want to be treated as charity cases. Sensing their pain, Carolyn went to the relief kitchens and brought food to them, which they accepted gratefully. Another symptom Carolyn noticed in herself was the sudden dread of any kind of rain or storm in the days that followed. Her fear was amplified many times over as she fought to control it.

In Wheatland, Mayor Helen Duby was facing the same intense fear of storms. She had never been afraid before. Now she found herself fighting the phobia back every time dark clouds appeared. She also joined many others in the feeling of unreality that followed. Her entire town had almost disappeared in front of her eyes. The tragedy created a strange perception that what she was going through seemed to be happening to somebody else. Nothing seemed to be real. And yet she was able to draw on almost superhuman strength to do the things she had to do in her job as mayor.

The psychological impact was just as great on those officials and rescue and relief workers as it was on the victims. Those who were supposed to be steeled to face tragedy, such as firemen, policemen, paramedics, and others, had a sort of double jeopardy: They were more or less expected to repress their own trauma because of their jobs. This was not easy.

When Police Chief George Keryan of Wheatland arrived back in town to find nearly all the familiar landmarks gone, he found himself in total shock. He felt that he didn't know where he was. The shock continued to stay with him as he went about the job of rescue and relief.

Rugged and brawny fire lieutenant John Hughes and police officer Joe Profato in Niles had braced themselves against psychological shock over many years of dealing with tragedy. Yet the terrible scenes at the Niles Park Plaza left indelible scars on them as they went about digging out severed bodies, piecing them together for identification, pulling out a stake impaling a victim on the ground, or desperately trying to lift an I-beam from a trapped victim. One scene continued to haunt Lieutenant Hughes: a daughter clinging to the hand of her mother who was trapped and killed under debris; he had to separate her forcibly. Joe Profato had to face the job of informing one man that his wife had been killed. Humanely, he had to postpone informing him; the shock would have been too great on the scene.

The repressed reactions would come out in different ways. Lieutenant Hughes found himself crying when over forty Boy Scouts arrived from Dearborn Heights, Michigan, to help with the cleanup. The gesture was so magnanimous that it released the pent-up reaction from the long hours of rescue work he had been doing without sleep. He had a similar reaction when the fire department of Xenia, Ohio, volunteered to send help. That town had been almost leveled by a killer tornado in 1974. They knew the resulting terror well. One resident there had been so unnerved that he slept fully dressed for weeks. Other people literally panicked whenever a storm warning was issued, some of them actually going down into sewers in the face of the threat. The scars remained long after the physical scars had been healed.

The tough and seasoned workers found it hard to walk away from the rescue efforts unaffected, even though they had been doing everything humanly possible to relieve the suffering. They, too, had their share of tornado guilt, that they were spared when others weren't. Fire Chief Herk Shearer in Albion had braced himself over the years to face anguish, yet he commented, "No matter how well prepared you are, you're bound to run into something that hits you hard." Or as one clinical psychologist put it, "No matter how strong a person is, whether he's a tough cop or National Guardsman or whatever, one can be terribly affected by a body, especially a child's, which is the most emotionally upsetting thing a person can experience."

Journalists also faced a similar situation in covering the story. Bob McClymond in Albion found it hard to maintain his objectivity. With friends and neighbors who had lost loved ones, and with a third of the homes in his own town literally blown away, it was hard to face his typewriter. It felt almost intrusive to write about his fellow townsmen who had suffered so much. He felt the

165

strange, awkward discomfort of tornado guilt, too, along with the others. The *News* building was missed by two blocks. His family was unharmed. The *News* staff was intact, even though Cheryl Podoll, who handled the advertising and page layout, had a narrow escape. She had just left the local pizza shop with her nine-year-old son as the tornado ripped through the town half a block away. She threw the boy facedown and lay on top of him and they were unscathed. After the whirlwind passed in a matter of seconds, she picked up her pizza and went home.

For several days, McClymond found it impossible to put anything down on paper. Meanwhile, helicopters from out of town swung into the air with reporters and television crews to bring the news to the world. McClymond envied their detachment. They streamed into the *News* office, which McClymond offered to them. He envied their objectivity, their electronic memory typewriters, and their modems that they connected to the phone for prompt dispatch. At one time there were reporters from the *Dallas Morning News,* the *Philadelphia Inquirer,* the *Chicago Tribune,* and the Associated Press crowded into the office. They were getting out the news to the world that the Albion tornado was the third worst in recorded history, and Bob McClymond wasn't particularly happy about that kind of recognition.

Not all the out-of-town reporters remained objective. Reporter Roy Seneca of the *Erie Morning News* drove down to cover the story shortly after it happened. He doubted if it was going to be much of a story, and was even a little bored as he drove toward Albion. He came across a long line of cars parked near the trailer park in Cranesville, just outside Albion. A young girl in her twenties was standing by a pile of rubble that once had been a house. Her legs were bloody and she appeared in shock. "My house! My house!" she kept repeating over and over. Beside it, not a single trailer was left standing. A few slabs of concrete, like gravestones, marked where they once stood.

Seneca drove on to Albion. Nearly every person he came across was muttering, "Oh, my God, I don't believe it." Then he saw the firemen carrying out the bodies of Stanley and Frances Kireta from what was left of their home, with stairs that led up to nowhere but the sky.

"It seemed hard to imagine that just two hours earlier the Kiretas were probably enjoying a dinner or relaxing at home on a warm afternoon," he wrote in his story. "Now there was nothing left. It was during the ride home that the emotion of what I saw began to hit me. I kept getting chills up and down my spine and I could not get the sad faces out of my mind. It was all so dreadfully sad and dreadfully real."

As a mental-health worker told Bob McClymond later, the impact on the town was felt by everyone, that everyone was a victim. He agreed. "A disaster like this certainly puts things in perspective," McClymond noted. "Things that were awfully important a few weeks ago seem relatively inconsequential now."

Yet getting out the local paper was important. People were craving news. Several newsboys made deliveries even though their own homes had been lost. Families searching through rubble took time out from clearing and cleaning to scrounge for newspapers that couldn't be delivered to nonexistent homes. Neighbors saved papers in their garages for the displaced people to come and get them. If any case could dramatize the importance of news, the situation in Albion and elsewhere confirmed it.

Staff writer Vicky Canfield had the same problems McClymond was facing. She started to type out the obituaries and broke down in tears. She could get through the job only by typing one, moving on to something else, then coming back to type the next. She concluded a first-person article by writing, "I am filled with a sense of awe concerning the force of nature and I hurt for those who find themselves face to face with the consequences. At the same time, I am heartened with the knowledge that while the tornado touched down in our little community, leaving havoc and destruction in its wake, it also touched the hearts of thousands of neighbors who placed compassion above their personal safety and comfort."

Vicky began to experience the same sort of symptoms that hundreds of her fellow townspeople were going through: insomnia, loss of appetite, and the omnipresent survivor or tornado guilt. There were times when she felt she was beginning to lose her mind.

When she interviewed counselor Jerry Erdley at the St. Vincent Health Center for an article, she was relieved to find that her reactions were perfectly normal in the aftermath of the tragedy.

Erdley was working free of charge at the health center and at the Hamot Medical Center, both in Erie. His experience in helping Vietnam veterans and his work with the National Post-traumatic Stress Conference were invaluable in the days that followed the catastrophe. The emotional scars of the tornado victims were parallel to those suffered by the veterans. The problems that arose were spontaneous, intrusive recollections and thoughts that suddenly would seize hold of a person, along with vivid nightmares. Also, the noise of a train or a plane could easily set off phobia, creating panic as vivid as that experienced during the tornado itself.

Then there were the emotional numbness, the feeling of being detached, and apathy more debilitating even than anger. There were violent mood swings and hyperalertness, or, in contrast, a stoic repression of all emotions that created an almost catatonic condition.

The latter could be most damaging. At times it would arise from the feeling that some people believed they actually were going insane, and wanted to hide this from others. They would avoid telling others that they were having nightmares or jumping every time they heard a noise. In other words, they felt they were mentally ill when they were not. As Dr. William Kowalski, a clinical psychologist in Erie, stated, ''These people are not crazy. There's nothing wrong with them. But they may need help for years to come.'' He stressed the importance of the victims being aware of what could happen in the months and years to come, that the symptoms could go from numbness to frustration to anger.

What Erdley and other mental-health counselors were attempting was to create an awareness that these symptoms were perfectly normal, and if this was recognized, the sufferer would at least feel reassured—even if the symptoms didn't disappear. The therapists made their services available twenty-four hours a day. They encouraged people to talk, talk, talk about their experiences with friends and clergy and seek counseling wherever possible. Otherwise the symptoms might continue for years.

Aware of such problems, volunteer counselors from churches throughout western Pennsylvania arrived in the area to help take the load off local pastors, who were being swarmed by those seeking spiritual and psychological help. The reactions would be going through three stages. The first stage was ameliorated by the urgency and action to find lost friends or relatives, to clear the debris, to help the distressed. At this stage the adrenaline flows freely, and action takes over to replace emotions. The second stage brings in a mix of emotions—the nightmares, the feelings of unreality, disbelief, helplessness, disorganization, frustration, and anger. At the third stage, more chronic symptoms arise, especially the deep-seated phobias that come up when least expected.

The Vietnam experience served as a template of what to expect. After the challenge of reconstruction was met, the deep impact could hit later. Rick Victor, a Vietnam veteran who knew how people could suffer in this way, came to Newton Falls and Niles a day after the storm to help in any way he could. He reported that he could see the stress in the eyes and faces of the people whose loss of homes was almost as anguishing as the loss of loved ones. He tried to get them to talk it out to him, helping them go through the grief process.

People in Albion expressed spontaneously their unconscious feelings of guilt. "It makes you feel kind of guilty in a way," Shirley Kauffer told an Erie reporter. "Many of us feel this way. We have the same feelings but hate to say it. You feel uncomfortable talking about it."

Ray Zimmerman, untouched by the storm, commented, "I just can't conceive of the neighbors being gone. I see them alive, even though I saw their bodies being pulled out of the rubbish."

Tod Hilliard lives on an Albion street where not a single house was damaged. "It makes you feel glad," he said, "but you can't believe why the tornado went the other way, away from us. It could have come this way. There was nothing left of my friend's home. It gives you a sense of responsibility to the community."

Another whose home was untouched was Harold Kleinfeld's on North Main Street. He reflected the feeling of many Albion residents who escaped without damage: "You have to feel awful for all those people. It's so strange that just one street over and two blocks down, everything is wiped out and here there's nothing damaged at all. You keep thinking about all those people over there."

Linda Stahlsmith, trying to conquer the overwhelming grief over little Luke's death in her arms, kept fighting to keep her tears back in public and was partly successful even though she continued to permit herself to burst into tears when she was alone. She worried, of course, about the trauma on the other children. Even Bryce, her youngest, pointed up to the sky and said, "Luke all gone."

Linda watched the other children carefully for aftershock and signs of depression. For a while there didn't appear to be any. But one day she found Luke's brother crying under a blanket, saying that he wanted Luke back. At another time, she found eight-year-old Brook bursting into tears when she was looking at the family's picture album. Nine-year-old Bree never cried at all—but at the first sign of a storm, she began shaking violently and continued to do so. Linda herself felt she could remain strong but soon recognized that she couldn't, especially in seeking the anxiety symptoms in her children.

In fact, children all through the region were especially vulnerable to post-traumatic shock syndrome. The sight of a dark cloud or a thunderstorm would trigger a violent reaction. Psychologists reasoned that this reaction would linger for years to come. Counseling and therapy were heavily recommended for children.

On the Monday following the death of Mrs. Elaine Italiano, both the faculty and the first-grade pupils of the Taft Elementary School in Niles were devastated by the news. She was astute and popular, considered an outstanding teacher by both pupils and peers. One little boy simply could not face coming to school. He asked his mother to clip out her picture from the paper that announced her death and keep it for him to remember her by. A little girl in the class made no comment when she learned the news that her teacher had been killed. Then, just as she got into bed, she asked her mother, "Mrs. Italiano is sleeping—right?"

Principal Mary Byrd Boyd called together a meeting of the thirty pupils in the first grade and the faculty in the Taft School library. She asked everyone to carry on in Elaine Italiano's spirit and encouraged the children—and teachers, too—to cry if they wanted to. Most of them did so, openly.

The outpouring of community support did much to alleviate the suffering, as much at least as could be expected under the horrifying circumstances. At the same time, the annoyance of constantly going through the National Guard and police posts was irksome. Some people couldn't get back to their homes to search for valuables. Others were unable to get satisfactory identification papers. Improvised passes were fashioned for residents, but it was slow and awkward to obtain them. Yet the presence of such outsiders as the National Guard, state troopers, and Red Cross or Salvation Army workers gave a strange psychological sense of security, a sense that there were outsiders who did care. Just seeing them there helped.

Outsiders who were not welcome were the gawkers and sightseers who came not to help but to stare. Numbed and stunned residents, fishing through their rubble looking for scattered possessions, did not enjoy being looked on as oddities, and they resented the stream of cars that cruised by filled with curiosity-seekers. But in general, there was a minimum of complaining. Reverend Polley in Atlantic claimed that he never heard anyone grumble, that people were more concerned how others were doing.

In addition to American flags stuck up on fragile poles in the piles of rubble that once were homes, there were signs in crude painted letters that reflected the mood of the people. Some were fashioned with grim humor: HOUSE FOR SALE—CHEAP; GIBSON'S ANNUAL YARD SALE; 100% DISCOUNT. Some were informational: ALL PERSONS ACCOUNTED FOR HERE. Some were inspirational: ALBIONITES—HANG IN THERE! WE LUV YA!, or: THE STEFFS ARE ALIVE AND WELL AND HERE TO STAY. WE ARE REBUILDING!

The tough sinew of the people was evident by a simple statement made by Pete Stebnisky, who had lived in Albion for thirty-two years. His sister lived in the house next door and was killed instantly when it exploded in the twister. Stebnisky said

171

when asked if he were going to move away from the shattered town: "We ain't gonna go anywhere!"

Then he dug through the rubble and found the only suit he could find without a hole in it. He got dressed and left to go to his sister's funeral.

AFTERWORD

I read in the press about the terrifying bursts of the killer tornadoes in Ohio, western Pennsylvania, and elsewhere during early June 1985.

Nature seemed to be violently restless all across the world during that season.

The headlines proclaimed it loudly: STORMS OF WIND, RAIN AND SNOW OVER EUROPE KILL AT LEAST 16, wrote *The New York Times*. Other stories told of the catastrophic tidal waves in Bangladesh, plus the earthquake potential on the West Coast. A headline in *U.S. News and World Report* asked: HURRICANES—TORNADOES—IS THE WORST YET TO COME?

It was apparent that weather often was the people's worst enemy, that at times it provoked severe crises in the population, and that few knew in detail the story behind these giant impersonal forces, or ways to ameliorate the dangers.

Among all this chaotic pandemonium, the tornadoes seemed the most ominous. I have always been morbidly curious about them since my first bookshelf encounter with Toto, Dorothy, and Oz.

I tried to picture in my mind's eye an image of the scenes that must have taken place in the towns and villages of the Ohio and

Pennsylvania countryside as the National Weather Service struggled with the mass of data that were sure to have foreshadowed a threatening Sword of Damocles that was about to come down from the sky. Obviously here were all the elements of tragic drama, with ominous forces gathering to explode on unsuspecting victims who still were unsuspecting in spite of heroic efforts on the part of the National Weather Service to forewarn in the face of a surly and mostly unpredictable enemy.

I finally set out for the survey in September, four months after the tornado assaults on the stricken countryside, but the ravages were far from forgotten.

My first step was to visit Kansas City, where the National Severe Storms Forecast Center of the National Weather Service is housed, where the center's director, Fred Ostby, and senior forecaster, Steve Weiss, had sat on the day of the fateful storms. I joined both of these meteorologists in front of the flickering computer terminal screens where they had watched the gathering omens of the storms that were to create one of the most powerful families of tornadoes to strike a heavily populated area of the country. Weiss and Ostby were both businesslike and cordial as they explained the intricacies of modern-day electronic forecasting. Most obvious was their dedication to and enthusiasm for their jobs—and their capacity to interpret the massive daily inflow of data swiftly and with authority. When Weiss pulled out the stack of charts from back on the day of the May 31 disaster I was almost startled to see the marked area he had blocked out for the afternoon's tornado watch. The area clearly defined a rectangle that included exactly every town in the path of the tornadoes that were to strike so brutally. Yet both Ostby and Weiss were hoping that the future computerized breakthroughs might make the forecasting more exact than the present state of the art permitted. "The problem is," Ostby said, "that of convincing people to take the watches and warnings seriously. Sociologists claim that people will do almost anything they can to deny they are under a risk. They think, 'We never get tornadoes here in our town.' This impedes the whole process and defeats the preparedness thing. This attitude was prevalent in Windsor Locks, Connecticut, in 1979 and in Worcester,

Massachusetts, in 1979. It was hard for the people there to understand that lots of places outside of Tornado Alley get hit hard. In 1969, for instance, one hurricane took out a motel where people had gathered for a "hurricane party." Over twenty people were killed. But I'd still rather face a hurricane than a tornado.

"You know thunderstorms are so common people naturally tend to ignore them," Ostby continued. "There are over a hundred thousand a year, and only one out of a hundred will carry a tornado with it. But two thirds of these tornadoes are weak, and the big killer tornadoes boil down to about twenty-five a year and account for about eighty percent of all people killed.

"There are so many things we run into. You get a deepening low-pressure system in the upper Mississippi Valley, moving eastward to the Great Lakes, and yet you might not get tornadoes. Actually, it was surprising that Steve Weiss put out a watch at all on May thirty-first. It was an extremely rapid development that literally exploded when the squall line suddenly developed along and ahead of the cold front. The cold front moves eastward; the warm front moves northward. They converge at low levels. Then the violent updrafts develop. We don't always need a cold front, however. Other systems can bring about converging air.

"What we call a cell is a cumulonimbus thunderhead, one of the thunderstorms that usually form along a cold front, not all with tornadoes. The speed at which they travel toward the east or northeast is a factor of the intensity. If the air is heavily laden with moisture and heat at low levels it is growing in its environment at a much faster rate than when it is just chugging along. It gets like a Pac-Man sort of thing. The moisture-rich rapid environment takes on its own rotation."

I asked Ostby if there were a visible separation between the cells, and he answered, "If you looked at the system from an airplane at sixty thousand feet it would look like a continuous sheet of clouds. If you looked with radar at the cores there might be random spacing between the updraft in one and the updraft in another, and they merge at times to become a supercell.

"The anvil is the last thing to disappear in a thunderhead. This cirrus cloud will loosen up with a downdraft, and the debris is left. You'd think the ice crystals would be first to go.'' I wanted to visualize the speeds within the tornado funnel and asked Ostby to help me do so. Since they can range up to over three hundred miles an hour, the results could only be horrific. "Think of a river of air going at such speeds, say, at two hundred miles an hour," Ostby continued. "Picture a log in it striking a house or a car. There would not be much left of either. There were certain elements that existed on the May thirty-first, 1985, outbreak that combined to build the incredible forces. There was the strong jet stream moving across the storm system at high altitude. Another factor was the instability of the atmosphere, often present in the spring of the year. The dry air came in above the surface moist air, creating an unusual dry-line situation all across the Ohio Valley. So there were the main parameters: jet stream, instability, and dry air above.''

I left the Kansas City center reluctantly with admiration for the job the staff was doing in spite of the present-day limitations. I prepared to fly to Ohio to track the storms from where the first touch-down had been reported. This would be taking me from Ravenna, Ohio, through Newton Falls, Niles, and on eastward to the chain of Pennsylvania communities that had been so savagely blasted. I steeled myself for what was certain to be a tragic sight, even though four months had passed since the disaster. I was, however, to be surprised.

There was no straight, clean line of a single tornado that had swept eastward from Ohio and into western Pennsylvania. The multiple funnels had split and leapfrogged along their deadly paths, and reports varied as to where the first touch-down had been. To try to trace the gouges would require a zigzag course, with several jogs to the north and south in doing so. The grim summary of a National Weather Service team had just been issued to punctuate the severity of the damage to the area. The teams found the weather to have been rare and unusual on that day, the deadliest in Pennsylvania history and the strongest twisters in eastern Ohio and western New York. Wheatland alone had been blasted by three-hundred-mile-an-hour winds, with seventeen fatalities. Few if any structures are built to stand this kind of fury. In Pennsylvania 1,009 houses were wiped out, and the resulting damage totaled nearly four hundred million dollars. Over seven hundred were injured in Pennsylvania and three hundred in Ohio, and the property damage mounted to over one hundred million dollars.

Driving from the Cleveland weather station south toward Newton Falls, I passed through Ravenna, Ohio, to find little sign there of the havoc that had struck its neighboring communities. In fact, the stark normalcy of the Americana scene was something of a surprise. It demonstrated evidence of the irony that a tornado can obliterate one piece of geography and leave an area untouched only a few inches away. Along with shaded lawns and pleasing white clapboard houses were all the accouterments of peaceful midwestern living: a Dairy Queen, a Pantry Food mart, a coin laundry, and a used-car lot. Route 5 continues eastward to narrow down through some wooded hills where sweet corn and fresh vegetables could be bought, and where a somber sign on a miles-long chain-link fence announced the presence of the Ravenna arsenal, where one funnel was said to have touched down. But no one was about to report having seen it, and the arsenal grounds seemed to be shrouded in secrecy. One police officer said, "There are twenty-two thousand acres inside that fence and nobody knows what goes on there." If the tornado did damage there, none was evident in a peek through the fence. Along the country road, however, some of the trees were stripped of their leaves—hardly a scene of a killer storm. But in Newton Falls, a flat stretch of black tarmac was the only evidence of the site where the post office once stood, just across the street from the police station where Clayton Reakes had stood to spot the tornado whirling toward Newton Falls. Down the street was the church bearing the sign WITH THE FAITH OF A MUSTARD SEED WE CAN MOVE MOUNTAINS. The sign reflected more than anything else the attitude I was to discover everywhere among the people even though buildings and forests still were leveled. In Albion, for instance, only the foundations of several rows of houses were visible, filled in with gravel that created domes reminiscent of the Indian burial mounds that once had been built in the region. But the spirit of the people reflected a quiet sense of resolve and determination even where the paths of the twisters still remained visible. I felt that I had learned a valuable lesson about humankind's "unconquerable soul."

Most interesting to me was what had gone on behind the scenes in the firing-line weather stations that were joining with the Kansas City National Severe Storms Forecast Center to coordinate the national picture with the regional picture. At Cleveland I talked at length with Marvin Miller and his National Weather Service staff about how they watched the meteorological picture build toward a climax on that frantic day.

Bitter experience has taught Marvin Miller to take severe storms and tornadoes seriously. "The spring of the year is when we have to keep our eyes open," he said. "That's when most of the tornadoes are likely to hit—especially killer tornadoes. We always keep a lookout for the most 'favorable' conditions. For a tornado you're likely to need a sharp declination between cold air and warm air. Most often that Canadian cold air is coming down. Then there's the low-level jet stream. When these three things meet, you've got to watch out.

"Of course, in order for us to do our job right," Miller continued, "we have to rely heavily on volunteers from the public. It's vital we get this help. Take what Clayton Reakes did in Newton Falls. He's been spotting for years even though the chances that he'll ever see one are small. We all feel he saved many lives on the May thirty-first, '85, outbreak. That's the kind of people we need."

Miller takes his message to the public constantly. "Yes," Miller continued, "I gave talks on thirty-four evenings in early '85 to try to get citizen groups going. I told them we're due for another big day of tornadoes because we have these big killer outbreaks every eight to twelve years in Ohio. In 1985, eleven years had gone by since we had a major outbreak, and I figured we were due. Later the media kept asking me how I figured the '85 outbreak was coming and I explained that past climatology indicated so. I talked to volunteer spotters, police, sheriff departments, ham radio clubs, and others. The talks foreshadowed the May thirty-first killers on the nose.

"But the skill of the Severe Storms Center has become more and more accurate in issuing tornado watches for us to the east of them over the last fifteen years. The computers they've developed have allowed their techniques to improve, relieve them of drudgery work, and give them a chance to keep up with things.

"Anyway," Miller continued, "I'm glad we're keeping up our program with the public, especially with the schools. We have a very active program with them. Last March we talked to schools of grades one through six. We invite them to participate in an original poster program and invite all the regional winners to Sea World. Then we determine state winners and honor them at the state fair. Some children have saved lives by telling their parents what to do.

"We feel good about getting the warnings out on time—and bad about missing them, of course."

I was able to persuade Miller and the others at the Cleveland weather station to describe the events of that hectic day of May 31, 1985.

"When Jerry Murphy called me very early that morning and asked me what time I was going to need him, I was pleased with his alertness. We're lucky to have a guy like Jerry as a Skywarn volunteer. You see, in spite of all our instruments, we're isolated from that 'ground truth' out under the open sky, and we need that feedback information constantly. Jerry was in the office within the hour and he stayed all day. The weather outside seemed to belie what our instrument readings were telling us. It was hazy and full of sunshine outside, very few clouds, and the sun was dominant. However, there was a tremendous amount of moisture in the air. This was baffling because our radar showed literally nothing in the way of clouds at one, two, or three in the afternoon. The screen was actually clear from eight in the morning until three.

"With still no action showing, Jerry told me, 'You might as well go home, there seems to be nothing doing.'

"I went out to his radio desk and then looked at the radar again. There was still nothing doing.

"But then between three fifty-five and five after four, everything started to build, with an enormous mass of supercells that seemed almost impossible to believe.

"Then the reports began coming back in with the 'ground truth.'

179

From Geauga County came reports of golf-ball-size hail, sixty-mile-an-hour winds. What was unusual about the situation was that eastern Ohio was in the path of the tornadoes, where in the past they strike for the most part to the west of the state. We were putting out a rash of severe-weather warnings as opposed to tornado warnings that still had to be held back until we got the 'ground truth' of them.

"It was about five-thirty when we lost our telephone lines to Youngstown, and as a result we had to pick up their responsibilities for Trumbull, Columbiana, and Mahoning counties, while the Pittsburgh weather office had to pick up for Mercer and Lawrence counties in Pennsylvania. I can't tell you how difficult it is to pick up for the other stations that are geared into the fire, police, and Skywarn units and the regular Emergency Broadcasting System AM and TV stations to reach the public and public officials in their own areas.

"Our NOAA weather wire is tied into our computer, which goes out to some hundred and fifty people, including the news media, highway patrol, and others. Our radar covers a hundred and twenty miles, sometimes farther under rare conditions. Jerry Murphy sends me all the information he gets from his contact with all the ham radio operators in Ohio. We depend on them to tell us the things we can't discern on radar, things like microbursts, surface winds, etc.

"In addition, we make one call to each county sheriff department and they use that to fan out to other police and fire departments. And once the decision is made to issue a warning we are typing it up electronically to the Emergency Broadcasting System via hotline to the stations at all times. This is radio station WWWE in our area. At the same time, the NOAA weather radio is activated with a tone alert."

Staff forecaster Jack May recalled his activity on the day of the great storms vividly.

"Marvin and I were here at seven-thirty that morning. There was a moderate risk for severe storms posted by Kansas City. Then the cold front that was going to trigger these storms, we were told, was going to cross the northwest corner of Ohio, and that the storms could develop at any time. It looked that way and we waited and waited, telling ourselves if this is going to break, it'll break big.

"About four-fifteen, I looked outside to the east and could see the storms starting to build, including the big anvil. Then the whole mess started to form a line. It blossomed, exploded, and began boiling. The heat on the surface was the trigger that started the atmosphere turning. The mess had started so close to Cleveland, where the ground clutter of the buildings obscured the screen.

"When I turned on the radar a little later I could see the storms all lined up. I grabbed a tape and made radio reports on the storms gathered over Trumbull and Geauga counties, and put the tape out over the air. The ground reports indicated that roofs were being blown off by a tornado that had passed through Mesopotamia. Marvin was typing up warnings one after the other and his arm would poke through the doorway while I read the warnings out over the radio.

"The Youngstown station went out between five and six—lightning, maybe. The power lines went down with the first waves that went through. Niles was in the third wave, I think. My responsibility was along the northern shore of Lake Erie. The Columbus weather station handled the other waves to the south.

"I knocked off at about eleven that night, hoping that I'd done some good and hoping also that the radio and TV stations got the warnings out over the air. I think the biggest problem is apathy and both the public and the media should be aware of this."

At the Erie and Pittsburgh "firing line" weather offices, the story was similar.

"The problem is that the forces of Nature are so great that they can dwarf all the ingenuity of modern technology in spite of its electronic wizardry. The forecasters are still left with a sense of frustration knowing that life or death of people can often rest on the information they are fighting to get out in the face of an intractable enemy." Director Dave Bell of the Erie weather station continued, "The day before the big outbreak, on Thursday, the data pointed to very severe weather. Everything was ripe for it but still nothing developed as it should have until that explosion happened right on top of us. We watched our radar reports from stations upstream, all the graphics and printouts from the national radar maps. There are several things we can interrogate anywhere in the country plus our own local radar. Whenever there's a strong cold front moving across the country, we gear up and watch carefully.

"When the big hit came we got three radar hooks at one time, a signature that indicates a tornado that has probably already touched down. We had the Albion hook clearly on the screen.

"What we do is scan the supercell horizontally, interrogate it, then lock in on the rotating top. Then we interrogate on the vertical and look for more signatures, like spikes, pendants, and more hook echoes. There's no guarantee we will find them; sometimes they are masked. If we pick up a hook right over the top of a town it's already hit hard. When we get the new Doppler radar we'll have a really improved system. The ordinary radar picks up water content and gives us wind shear and wind direction. It will also show up the development of a tornado about fifteen minutes before it touches down. So we'll have a much better chance to warn people. On our conventional radar we can't be absolutely sure we're going to see the hook, although as I mentioned we did spot the Albion hook down in Crawford County, and a second and third in Wheatland and Pymatuning and they were moving eastward, but it was such an explosive layer cake we had little lead time. One of the problems was that usually we would learn about severe storms coming this way from out in western Ohio. But nothing was happening out there as late as three in the afternoon—not even a little rain shower. It wasn't until three-thirty that we discovered a few thunderstorms popping up. Prior to that in the morning or early afternoon all the radars in the whole area weren't showing any precipitation of any kind.

"Of course, we got Steve Weiss's tornado watch from Kansas City at four twenty-five P.M., when it came in over our AFOS, or automated link-up system. We get a flashing light and a tone alert. Then we hit a button to bring up a full picture of the situation on the screen. From this we plot a box designating all the areas in the tornado-watch sectors. We're responsible for several counties here, including Crawford, Warren, McKean, Venango, Forest, Elk, and Cameron.

"Our procedure is to find out which of these is going to be affected by this watch and then put out a NOAA weather radio notice informing these counties that they're included in the watch. Another big problem is that some of the fire companies don't even have NOAA radio receivers.

"After an event like this, you sit back and try to think of ways you could warn people better. You just can't get up and run down the street."

APPENDIX A

It wasn't until October 1985 that the full disaster survey report of a special National Weather Service team was issued, headed by Rear Admiral Kelly E. Taggart, director of the Office of NOAA Corps. The team included Richard Waggoner, chief of the Operations Division of the National Weather Service in Silver Spring, Maryland, and several other chief officials of the National Weather Service from various operational divisions. Included also was Professor Gregory Forbes of the Department of Meteorology of Pennsylvania State University. They moved through the damaged areas of Ohio and Pennsylvania to survey and analyze an overall picture of the disaster, correlating and correcting some of the conflicting reports of the number of casualties and sparsely reported information. The team pieced together a full picture of the erratic and fitful activity of the unprecedented outbreak, tracking the paths of the multiple twisters and examining in minute detail the results of the fateful day, especially those elements that could not be assessed during the heat of the battle.

The team recalled that the new outbreak was totally unprecedented in the stricken areas of Ohio and Pennsylvania. The latter state suffered the most tornadoes it had ever experienced in a single day. Here sixty-nine were killed on that day, which equaled the total number of tornado deaths in Pennsylvania since 1916.

The survey team emphasized that a major lesson learned from the May 31, 1985, disaster was that tornadoes can hit with a vengeance regardless of the location or the terrain, while it had once been thought that mountains and hills could break up a tornado's fury.

The survey team had high praise for the work of the National Severe Storms Forecast Center in Kansas City and praised the professionalism, dedication, and motivation of the staff there. The team also had high praise for the National Weather Service forecast offices down the line in addition to the amateur radio storm spotters who had performed so ably for the local weather offices. The team also urged the National Weather Service to continue to recruit, train, and maintain the entire Skywarn volunteer operation. This was noted to be crucial in getting life-saving information to the public. The "fanout" of warning, it was noted, depended on multiple communication systems, and that NOAA weather radio was vital in this. The National Weather Service often utilized the NOAA weather wire teletypewriter service at increasing cost over the years. This in turn has pushed the commercial stations of the Emergency Broadcasting System to tape and replay NOAA weather radio warnings. Other units coordinating with the National Weather Service include state enforcement communication systems and state emergency management agency communication systems, which all play an important part in getting out weather information. The survey team emphasized that a continued exploration should be carried out to provide warning information to all these channels efficiently.

The importance of community awareness was emphasized in the survey team's report, which is the final step in the warning process.

In this regard the team cited the work of Captain Reakes in Newton Falls, noting that his community awareness was responsible in saving many lives.

Although nine people died in Trumbull County, none died in Newton Falls, and the survey team said that without Captain Reakes's work the death toll would have been much higher downstream on the tornado track, especially in Niles, where two seventy-five-thousand-pound oil tanks were lifted and thrown across a thoroughfare like cardboard cartons. The team made an overall recommendation to implement new ways of automating and speeding up warnings to the primary radio stations of the Emergency Broadcasting System, because even minor delays were critical. Others have noted that viewers looking at HBO or other cable broadcasts had no opportunity to catch the warnings, and that relatively few television sets were in use during the daytime hours. Also, no single communication system was found to be adequate, and the team recommended that multiple systems be utilized wherever possible to include warnings for state, local, and broadcast media. In the latter case solid relationships between the weather stations and the media had to be developed, especially through regular workshops.

Summarizing the onslaught, the report of the team pointed out that in only four hours, twenty minutes, 75 people were instantly killed, with 1,023 injured, and 2,350 homes destroyed, with 500 more heavily damaged. Twelve people more were killed in Canada and one woman killed in Wisconsin earlier in the day by the same storm system, thus bringing the official toll to 88. A total of twenty-eight tornadoes developed in the United States—seventeen of them in Pennsylvania, ten in northeastern Ohio, and one in southwestern New York. Three of the twisters were border crossers from Ohio to Pennsylvania, and three crossed from Pennsylvania to New York. In addition, thirteen more tornadoes were reported in Canada.

Although no one in the United States was aware of it at the time the tornado outbreak in Ontario began two hours earlier than in the United States and some two hundred miles north of the border. At this time—about 3:30 P.M.—the skies in the Great Lakes region were clear of thunderstorms. There was a broad area of blowing dust whipped up by strong surface winds behind the cold front and driven by an unusually intense low-pressure system over Lake Superior as the weather moved eastward. The winds aloft were increasing, adding to the power of the gusts on the surface. One intense gust caused a covered walkway to collapse in Lansing, Michigan, where a seventy-seven-year-old woman was killed at about eleven in the morning. In addition, two Wisconsin men were killed by a flying plank ripped from a ball-field bleacher.

It is interesting that only four of the twister touch-downs occurred after dark.

Other statistical breakdowns in the survey team report give a summary picture of the outbreak in mathematical form (see Appendix B).

From these and other figures the survey team made several observations. Fatalities in Albion totaled seventeen, the most in any single community. With fatal injuries in twenty-nine other communities, nine of those killed apparently took proper precautions to seek shelter but died in spite of it, mostly where houses were inadequately anchored to their foundations. Many houses were lifted off their foundations intact, in which cases many people were carried away with their homes. There was an unusually high number of violent tornadoes, seven in Pennsylvania alone, with the especially intense F-5 twister in Wheatland. The outbreak amounted to the strongest ever recorded in the region.

The survey team pointed out the long-term impact in, for instance, Albion, where the major employer had moved out two years earlier, where only half the high-school graduates remain in the town, and where many of the aging in the community have moved to warmer climates, thus eliminating one third of the tax base. In Wheatland 95 percent of its industry had been severely damaged and 84 percent of its industrial tax base eliminated by the tornado. In Atlantic the town secretary indicated that the town could not afford to give rebates on taxes already collected on 2,985 properties, even though those properties were gone.

In Atlantic the unusual character of the Amish community was noted. They showed little indication of moving away. Through their own cooperative efforts they had rebuilt much of their property on their own before federal and state disaster funds became available.

The disaster team did not confine its attention to the May 31, 1985, outbreak exclusively, although there was much the public at large could learn from it. Few knew the broad picture of tornadoes and their history. The sheer weight of the detailed facts would indicate the lethal force and widespread extent of the havoc nationally. Complacency should not be fostered generally. The lessons were bitter not only from the May 1985 outbreak but also from others, many of which were more fatal but most of which had taken place in the conventional Tornado Alley, where the public was more alert to the watches and warnings of the National Weather Service. The team reemphasized that the 1985 outbreak dramatized that vicious tornadoes could happen anywhere in spite of the terrain, a fact that should shake the complacency of residents in areas where tornadoes have been infrequent.

A review of general tornado facts in the report pointed out many grim statistics well worth mulling over for residents in any part of the country (see Appendix B).

In addition, the team's review of safety rules provides considerable food for thought (see Appendix B).

Although the team did not cover in detail the future developments contemplated by the National Weather Service, there are some hopeful projects in the works that may make warnings much more timely in the face of all-too-prevalent public apathy. The techniques development movement of the National Severe Storms Forecast Center is pushing ahead with organized research to aid in difficult decisions of severe storm prediction, under the direction of meteorologist Fred Mosher, to bridge the gap between theory and front-line forecasting. The forecaster still will have to make the final decision, but the new tools will give him a more articulate basis on which to do so. Although the Doppler has already shown a capacity to probe into the heart of an approaching deadly supercell, it has its weaknesses. It can detect the rotation inside the cumulonimbus cloud as it whirls faster to create the actual tornado. The signal is weak, however, when there is no precipitation inside the rotating cell. The Weather Service has only a handful of experimental Dopplers in use. The problem is classic: time and money. The Reagan administration has been cutting costs on programs under a directive from the federal Office of Management and Budget, and this has slowed progress considerably. Eventually the technology is expected to come up with an answer that will make an intelligible warning possible for up to a twenty-minute lead time. Estimates are that it will take up to 1992 to deploy.

The system will be called NEXRAD, and it will not be merely a radar system. It will be able to discern flash-flood-intensity rains, wind, wind shear, and turbulence plus temperature and dew-point differences and up to thirty different features on the screen. It will receive a return even in clear air, spotting almost invisible dust particles. It will be able to slice a storm cell in any direction in the manner of a CAT scan X ray, using a conical scan. It will take about five minutes to cover an entire cell system. Present-day radar can determine the height of a thunderhead, but NEXRAD will be able to determine conditions anywhere in the storm simply by picking out appropriate points. Since all tornadoes come from rotation within thunderstorms, NEXRAD's ability to spot and analyze them will mean that the forecaster will have a really efficient tool to work with. Plans call for an interactive process that combines with satellite and other data of the CSIS system, and the system will be installed in many weather service offices throughout the country. To be effective, the elements of the NEXRAD system must be no more than a hundred miles apart. This and other new technological advances as well as improved meteorological understanding of severe-weather development will require a complete reorganization of the whole National Weather Service, a major job as turbulent as the weather itself, with considerable political jockeying as to where the reorganized offices will be located.

Another important new aid for the future is a system called AWIPS-90, standing for Advanced Weather Processing System. This not only will bring CSIS capability to the local stations but also will provide them with the means to make immediate and short-term forecasts where minutes and seconds count so heavily. The AWIPS system is only in the specification stage, however, and eventual installation will not be ready before 1990.

Present-day weather balloons carrying radiosonde equipment to the troposphere provide a slow and clumsy way of probing the layers of the atmosphere, dispatching information only twice a day. A new Doppler-type computerized system called Wind

Profiler will be able to shoot straight up and get a continuous reading of the winds aloft. Data then will be available to process information about squall lines, severe storms, hail, and tornadoes on a much smaller scale than at present. Tuning the system will clearly show wind as a function of height. Due to be installed in 1988, Wind Profiler will be followed by Temperature Profiler in 1990.

Also in the future is a new remote sensing device called ASOS, which will automate all surface observations with minimum human intervention—a giant step ahead for speeding up weather prediction.

A constant probe into the mysteries of the tornado has been carried out over the years in several parts of the country. Chief among the meteorologists in the attempt to understand the tornado's surly behavior is Professor T. Theodore Fujita, the leading exponent in tornado research, at the University of Chicago.

Dr. Fujita has a passionate obsession about such meteorological monsters that amounts to an intense love-hate affair. He will use every effort to chase a tornado if there's even a remote chance of observing one firsthand, an event he has not yet been able to accomplish. He has followed more than two thousand miles of tornado tracks, however, and reconstructed a picture of the speeds within the funnels, out of which has come the standard tornado scale ratings, from F-0 to F-5.

Other research has been energetically pursued by meteorologists at Norman, Oklahoma, with a device called the Totable Tornado Observatory, or TOTO, an acronym inspired by Dorothy's feisty dog in *The Wizard of Oz*.

A brash team of scientists has been hell-bent in placing this four-hundred-pound canister of instruments directly in the path of a tornado to measure its wind speed and direction, temperature, electrical activity, and pressure. With such data widely available, forecasters might be better able to predict exactly where a twister might touch down.

The adventures of the TOTO scientists have been hair-raising as the team chases across the wide plains of Tornado Alley, attempting to place the steel cylinder so that it will be directly under a funnel, and then escape with their lives.

191

Results have not lived up to expectations. One attempt actually succeeded in Oklahoma, but the tornado that was measured was only of F-0 force, with winds of only hurricane strength. Direct measurement of a killer tornado still remains unrecorded, and new ideas are being considered to catch the elusive villains without the instruments being obliterated.

Further work is being conducted at the National Center for Atmospheric Research in Boulder, Colorado, where scientists are working on mathematical models and supercomputers that will combine forecasting theory with practical meteorology. Such work will fine-tune all weather predictions.

Researchers at the New Mexico Institute of Mining and Technology have used small airplanes to launch rockets loaded with probes into the guts of tornadoes. Although the rockets have yet to prove themselves, scientists hope this technique will help improve predictions of tornado behavior.

All these advances are directed at one goal: to be able to pinpoint better life-saving parameters. The missing gap that was tragically evident in the killer tornadoes of May 31, 1985, was getting out the news to the public in spite of the yeoman efforts of the National Weather Service.

Steve Weiss was able to pinpoint exactly the general areas of the twisters with uncanny accuracy seven hundred to eight hundred miles away. Tornado Watch Number 211 went out forty-five minutes before the first twister struck. The local weather offices spilled out that tornado watch and other warnings repeatedly. NOAA weather radio did the same. Commercial Emergency Broadcasting System stations, trained spotters, and TV stations did likewise. Fire sirens sounded, but many were cut short as power lines were severed by the storms.

The observations were correct, but the Paul Revere link showed weaknesses, perhaps because of public apathy. Many in the public still are not clear about the difference between a tornado watch and a tornado warning. Stations now are being encouraged to point out that a tornado warning is a call to immediate action, while a tornado watch means to be on the alert and prepared to take action.

NOAA weather radio frequencies are not included in normal

consumer radio sets, but for a few extra dollars they could be included and even required by law, with a tone alert built in.

It is possible that in every county communication center a computer phone could be installed that would sound off automatically in every area in the path of a tornado.

There is no question that killer tornadoes like those of May 31, 1985, will continue to happen year after year. Meanwhile, the devastation in lives and property can be a tragic reminder that no region of the country is immune from such havoc.

APPENDIX B

Tornado Facts

Tornadoes have occurred in all fifty states but are most frequent in the Southeast and the plains states. Although tornadoes can occur anytime during the year, the general season begins in late winter in the Deep South and moves northward to the Midwest by spring and to the upper Midwest during the summer.

- Average number of tornadoes per year, 1959–81: 735.

- In 1979 there were 849 tornadoes; in 1980, 864; in 1981, 774.

- Average number of fatalities from tornadoes, 1962–81: 94.

- In 1979 there were eighty-four deaths from tornadoes, including forty-two in Wichita Falls on April 10. In 1980, twenty-eight fatalities from tornadoes, including five killed at Kalamazoo, Michigan, on May 13, and five dead at Grand

Island, Nebraska, on June 3. In 1981, twenty-four fatalities from tornadoes, the lowest on record, including five killed at Bixby, Oklahoma, on April 19, and four dead at Cardington, Ohio, on June 13.

- The granddaddy of all tornadoes occurred on March 18, 1925, when 689 people were killed over a path of 220 miles through southern Missouri, Illinois, and Indiana.

- Codell, Kansas, was hit by tornadoes in 1916, 1917, and 1918 on the same day, May 20.

- Average wind speeds in a tornado range from one hundred to three hundred miles per hour (estimated).

- The average tornado is one-eighth mile wide; tornadoes range from a few feet to over a mile in width.

- The average forward speed of a tornado is thirty-five miles per hour; forward speeds range from nearly zero to over seventy miles per hour.

- The average path length of a tornado is two miles; path lengths range from a few yards to more than two hundred miles.

- The average time of a tornado on the ground is ten minutes; ground time ranges from a few seconds to three hours.

- Deaths from tornadoes in the United States, 1940–84: 5,419; from floods, 5,177; from hurricanes, 1,943.

Tornadoes are classified as weak, strong, or violent:

- Weak tornadoes comprise 62 percent of the total but cause only 2 percent of the fatalities.

- Strong tornadoes comprise 36 percent of the total and cause 30 percent of the fatalities.

AUTHOR'S NOTE

Shortly after I had completed the research on *Tornado,* I heard on my battery radio a clear statement that a tornado watch had been declared for an area twenty miles due west of Bridgeport, Connecticut.

This happened to be almost the exact location of my house. I called a few neighbors and suggested that they prepare for the possibility of going down to their basements until the watch was lifted.

I'm afraid I got a rather severe ribbing for being so cautious.

I took my wife and child down to our basement and waited out the possible storm, but nothing whatever happened.

In fact, I felt a little ashamed for my caution. But in going over my research I concluded that I'd rather feel ashamed than sorry.

That I feel a little paranoia now and then won't hurt anyone. And listening to and heeding the National Weather Service watches and warnings is far from being paranoid, I'm now convinced!

INDEX

Index

Index